Guide to the
History of Cartography

An Annotated List of References on the History of Maps and Mapmaking

Compiled by WALTER W. RISTOW

Geography and Map Division

Reference Department

LIBRARY OF CONGRESS WASHINGTON 1973

Library of Congress Cataloging in Publication Data

Ristow, Walter William, 1908-
   Guide to the history of cartography.

   First and 2d editions issued by the Library's Map
Division under title: A guide to historical cartography.
   1. Cartography—History—Bibliography. I. United
States. Library of Congress. Geography and Map
Division. II. United States. Library of Congress.
Map Division. A guide to historical cartography.
III. Title.
Z6021.R57   016.5269'8   73-9776
ISBN 0-8444-0097-1

For sale by the Superintendent of Documents, U.S. Government Printing Office
Washington, D.C., 20402 - Price: 75 cents   Stock Number 3001-00055

Preface

The Library of Congress published in 1954 *A Guide to Historical Cartography* which I compiled in collaboration with Mrs. Clara E. LeGear. A slightly expanded, revised edition of the *Guide* was published in 1960 and reprinted in 1962. Both editions were limited in scope and included only those references selected as being most pertinent for the study of cartographical history.

During the past decade or so the literature on the history of mapmaking has been greatly enriched and augmented. Over the same period there has been a heightened interest in the study of maps and mapmakers of the past. Both of these developments are reflected in this compilation, which includes almost six times as many entries as the 1960 edition of the *Guide*.

The present edition describes noteworthy general works as well as references relating to individual countries and to specialized aspects of cartography. A particular effort has been made to include cartobibliographies and other aids to the study of the cartographical history of the United States and the separate states. With a few exceptions the cited titles are monographs. For individual articles relating to various aspects of the history of American mapmaking, the user is referred to *Writings on American History* and other guides to cartographical and historical literature. The period of coverage in this compilation includes references for the 19th and early 20th century as well as those for earlier periods in cartographical history.

Publication in recent years of facsimile editions of many rare historical maps and atlases has also facilitated historical cartographical study and research. Many such reproductions are listed in *Facsimiles of Rare Historical Maps,* prepared in the Geography and Map Division and published, in periodic revisions, by the Library of Congress.

Titles in this volume are arranged in alphabetical order by author or by first word in the title. Library of Congress call numbers are given for all entries. Annotations amplify the bibliographic descriptions and call attention to distinctive contributions of particular references. The alphabetical index provides an approach to subjects, geographic areas, and other contributors.

Because this bibliography is concerned with the literature on the history and evolution of maps and mapmaking and not specifically with historical maps, the title has been changed to *Guide to the History of Cartography*.

I am indebted to those members of the Geography and Map Division staff who assisted me in preparing this guide.

Walter W. Ristow, *Chief*
Geography and Map Division

Contents

Annotated List of References

1

Acta cartographica. v. 1- 1967- Amsterdam, Theatrum Orbis Terrarum. tri-annual. illus., maps.   GA101.A2

"A series of monographs and studies on the history of cartography, re-printed from periodicals since 1800." Each issue contains between 10 and 20 articles in English, French, German, Spanish, Italian, or Dutch. As of January 1973, 14 volumes had been published.

2

Adonias, Isa. A cartografia da região amazônica; catálogo descritivo: 1500-1961 [por] Isa Adonias [com a colaboração da Sra. Maria de Lourdes Jovita] Rio de Janeiro, Instituto Nacional de Pesquisas da Amazônia, 1963. 2 v. illus., maps.   Z6027.A4A3

Lists maps, plans, and atlases relating to the Amazon region of Brazil, from the period of the discoveries to 1961. Arrangement is chronological under "South America and Brazil," followed by chronological listings under sepa-rate regions. Includes descriptions of maps in atlases, monographs, and serial publications. Annotations are comprehensive and bibliographic references are given for many items.

3

Afetinan, A. Life and works of the Turkish admiral: Pirî Reis; the oldest map of America, drawn by Pirî Reis. Translated by Dr. Leman Yolaç. Ankara, Türk Tarih Kurumu basimevi, 1954. 64 p. illus.   GA1033.5.P5A64

Pirî Reis lived from 1470 to 1554. The American segment of his world map of 1513 is preserved in the Palace of Topkapu, Istanbul. Reis' map is believed to have been based, in part, on a map drawn by Columbus.

4

Agee, Rucker. Maps of Alabama: the evolution of the state exhibited in printed maps from the Age of Discovery; a preliminary catalogue. [Birmingham, Ala., Public Library, 1955] unpaged.   Z6027.A25A4

There is an introductory essay on the "Cartography of Alabama."

5

Akademiíà nauk SSSR. *Institut etnografii.* Atlas of geographical discoveries in Siberia and North-Western America, XVII-XVIII centuries. Edited with an introduction, by A. V. Yefimov. Moskva, Nauka, 1964. 134 p. maps.

G2180.A4 1964 G&M

In Russian, with English translations of titles, summary of the foreword, and a list of the maps. There are reproductions and descriptions of 194 maps. "The object of this Atlas is to show how the geographic conceptions of the North-East of Asia and the North-West of America . . . historically originated and were specified; how the Russians' advent to the northeastern extremity of Asia set before them the task of discovering north-western America from Asia."

6

Alavi, S. M. Ziauddin. Arab geography in the ninth and tenth centuries. Aligarh, Dept. of Geography, Aligarh Muslim University, 1965. 134 p. illus., maps. (Aligarh, India. Muslim University. Dept. of Geography. Publication no. 2)   G93.A45

Bibliography: p. [119]-125.

The emphasis is on geography, but there are references to Arab cartography and reproductions of a number of early world maps by Arab cartographers.

7

Albion, Robert G., *ed.* Exploration and discovery. New York, Macmillan [1965] 151 p. (Main themes in European history)   G80.A45

Includes 13 papers, by 11 authors, on various subjects relating to exploration and discovery. There are bibliographic references following each chapter.

8

Albuquerque, Luis G. M. de. Introdução à história dos descobrimentos. Coimbra, Atlântida, 1962. 429 p. illus.   G89.A4

An introduction to the history of discoveries, this is one of the volumes prepared to commemorate the 450th anniversary of the death of Prince Henry the Navigator. Emphasis is on Portuguese discoveries. There is a lengthy bibliography (p. 401-426).

9

Almagià, Roberto. Monumenta cartographica vaticana iussu Pii XII P. M. consilio et opera procuratorum Bibliothecae Apostolicae Vaticanae. [Città del Vaticana, Biblioteca apostolica vaticana, 1944-55] 4 v. maps.

G1025.A4 1944 Map

Contents.—v. 1. Planisferi, carte nautiche e affini dal secolo XIV al XVII esistenti nella Biblioteca apostolica vaticana, 156 p., 56 plates of maps.—v. 2.

Carte geografiche a stampa di particolare pregio o rarità dei secoli XVI e XVII esistenti nella Biblioteca apostolica vaticana, 130 p., 40 plates of maps. —v. 3. Le pitture murali della Galleria delle carte geografiche, 89 p., 52 plates.—v. 4. Le pitture geografiche murali della terza loggia e di altre sale vaticane, 43 p., 28 plates.

A magnificent contribution to the history of cartography from the 14th through the 17th centuries. It contains extensive descriptions of the maps reproduced and has many bibliographical references.

10
— — — Monumenta Italiae cartographica. Riproduzioni di carte generali e regionali d'Italia dal secolo XIV al XVII. Raccolte e illustrate da Roberto Almagià. Firenze, Istituto Geografico Militare, 1929. 88 p. 65 plates of maps.
G1983.A4 1929 G&M

Includes biographical sketches of Italian mapmakers as well as critical evaluations of the maps they produced.

11
American Congress on Surveying and Mapping. *Technical Division on Property Surveys.* Bibliography of property surveying literature, compiled by Winfield H. Eldridge. Edited by Robert C. Eller. Washington, American Congress on Surveying and Mapping, 1963. 142 p. Z5853.S89A46

There are 1,065 entries, a number of which have historical cartographical interest.

12
American Geographical Society of New York. Research Catalogue. Boston, G. K. Hall, 1962. 15 v. maps. Z6009.A48

— — — — — — Map supplement. Boston, G. K. Hall, 1962. 26 p.
Z6009.A48 Suppl.

Includes references in monographic and serial publications, a number of which relate to the history of cartography.

13
American Geographical Society of New York. *Map Dept.* Index to maps in books and periodicals. Boston, G. K. Hall, 1968. 10 v. Z6028.A5

"Entries are arranged according to subjects and geographical-political divisions in one alphabet. Within each geographical division the arrangement is chronological." Many maps of historical interest are included in this index.

14
Amsterdam. *Nederlandsch Historisch Scheepvaart Museum.* De Blaeu's; beschrijvers van land-, hemel- en waterwereld. Amsterdam, Historisch Museum, 1952. 22 p. illus., maps. GA923.6.B6A6

A catalog of 152 items by or relating to the three generations of the Blaeu family and their works. In Dutch, with a one-page English summary.

15

Andrews, Michael C. The study and classification of medieval mappae mundi. Archaeologia, v. 75, 1926: 61-76. maps.   DA20.A64, v. 75

A clear and simple introduction to the study of medieval world maps. Includes a useful table which divides the known mappae mundi into families, divisions, genera, and species.

16

Anthiaume, A. Cartes marines, constructions navales, voyages de découverte chez les Normands, 1500-1650, par l'abbé A. Anthiaume ... Préface de l'amiral Buchard. Paris, E. Dumont, 1916. 2 v. illus.   GA231.A6

A treatise on French portolan charts and the discoveries and explorations made in the New World by Frenchmen. Volume 1 is devoted to charts and volume 2 to explorations.

17

Arden-Close, *Sir* Charles Frederick. The early years of the Ordnance Survey. A reprint with a new introd. by J. B. Harley and with an index added. New York, A. M. Kelley, 1969. 164 p. illus., maps.   GA66.G7A7 1969

"Reprinted from the Royal Engineers journal."
A reprint of the 1926 ed. published in Chatham by the Institute of Royal Engineers.

"Close's monograph, despite its rough-hewn character, will remain both an indispensable source book and—above all—a personal, eminently readable account of the founding personalities of our national survey."—Introduction.

18

Armstrong, Charles E. Copies of Ptolemy's Geography in American libraries. New York Public Library. Bulletin, v. 66, Feb. 1962: 105-114.
                              Z881.N6B, v. 66

"The New York Public Library is fortunate in having an almost complete collection of the various editions of the Geography." This compilation covers editions published between 1475 and 1730 that have been located in American libraries, with a total of 813 copies.

19

Averdunk, Heinrich, *and* J. Müller-Reinard. Gerhard Mercator und die Geographen unter seinen Nachkommen. Gotha, J. Perthes, 1914. 188 p. (Petermanns Mitteilungen. Ergänzungsheft nr. 82)   G1.P44 no. 182

An authoritative study of the geographical contributions of Gerardus Mercator, his contemporaries, and his successors.

20

Bachmann, Emil. Wer hat Himmel und Erde gemessen] Von Erdmessungen, Landkarten, Polschwankungen, Schollenbewegungen, Forschungsreisen und Satelliten. 2., überarb. Aufl. Thun, München, Ott [1968] 296 p. illus.

GA201.B2 1968

Bibliography: p. 296.

The history of surveying and mapping from the earliest time to the space age.

21

Baddeley, John F. Russia, Mongolia, China; being some record of the relations between them from the beginning of the XVIIth century to the death of the Tsar Alexei Mikhailovich, A.D. 1602-1676; rendered mainly in the form of narratives dictated or written by the envoys sent by the Russian tsars, or their voevodas in Siberia, to the Kalmuk and Mongol khans & princes, and to the emperors of China; with introductions, historical and geographical; also a series of maps showing the progress of geographical knowledge in regard to northern Asia during the XVIth, XVIIth & early XVIIIth centuries. The texts taken more especially from manuscripts in the Moscow Foreign Office Archives. New York, B. Franklin [196-?] 2 v. illus., maps. DK68.A2B3 1960z

Reprint of 1919 ed. published in London by Macmillan.

The introduction to volume 1 (p. xcviii-ccxvi) includes a summary cartographical history of the 16th to 18th centuries.

22

Bagrow, Leo. A. Ortelii Catalogus cartographorum. Gotha, J. Perthes, 1928-30. 2 v. maps. (Petermanns Mitteilungen. Ergänzungsheft no. 199 [und 210])

G1.P44, no. 199, 210

Contents.—v. 1. A-L.—v. 2. M-Z.

A biobibliographical study of Abraham Ortelius, his *Theatrum Orbis Terrarum,* and the 87 cartographers whose maps were included in the *Theatrum.* A comprehensive survey of 16th-century cartography, with an index.

23

– – – Die Geschichte der Kartographie. Berlin, Safari-Verlag [1951] 383 p. illus., maps.   GA201.B3

"Verzeichnis der Kartographen": p. [329]-371.
"Literatur-Verzeichnis": p. [377]-383.

An excellent introduction to the history of cartography with numerous illustrations, a classified bibliography, and biographical sketches of a large number of mapmakers. See also items 24, 25, and 200 for revised versions.

24

– – – History of cartography. Rev. and enl. by R. A. Skelton. [English translation by D. L. Paisey] Cambridge, Harvard University Press, 1964. 312 p. illus., maps.   GA201.B313 1964

Bibliography: p. 283-300.

Also published in London by C. A. Watts, 1964.   GA201.B313 1964a

A translation of item 23, with editorial revision and supplements by R. A. Skelton, former Superintendent of Map Room, British Museum. "In this English edition, some rearrangement of Bagrow's text has been carried out; a few linking passages have been inserted; and brief notes, mainly of bibliographical character, have been added." Some new illustrations, including a number in color, have also been added.

25

Bagrow, Leo, *and* R. A. Skelton. Meister der Kartographie [Berlin, Safari-Verlag, 1963] 579 p. illus., maps.   GA201.B3 1963

Bibliography: p. [539]-558.

Published in 1951 under the title *Die Geschichte der Kartographie,* the present edition is based on the English-language edition by R. A. Skelton, as translated into German by H. Thiemke. See also items 23 and 24.

26

Baker, John N. L. The history of geography; papers. New York, Barnes & Noble [1963] 266 p. illus.   G96.B25 1963a

Also published in Oxford by Blackwell [1963]   G96.B25 1963

A collection of papers by Baker, assembled and published on the occasion of his retirement from the Bursarship of Jesus College, Oxford University. The emphasis is on geographical history, but several of the papers relate to the history of maps, e.g., "Some Dutch Charts of the Seventeenth Century," and "The Earliest Map of H. Moll."

27

Baltimore. Museum of Art. The world encompassed; an exhibition of the history of maps held at the Baltimore Museum of Art October 7 to November 23, 1952. Organized by the Peabody Institute Library, the Walters Art Gallery [and] the John Work Garrett Library of the Johns Hopkins University in cooperation with the Baltimore Museum of Art. Baltimore, Trustees of the Walters Art Gallery, 1952. 125 p. illus., maps.   GA190.B2B2

Some 282 maps are described, with reproductions of 40 of them. Excellent cartobibliographical information.

28

Barbosa, Antonio. Novos subsídios para a história da ciência náutica portuguesa da época dos descobrimentos. Porto, Instituto para a Alta Cultura, 1948. 332 p. illus., maps.   VK549.B3

Bibliography: p. 325-330.

Includes considerable information about navigation charts of the 14th, 15th, and 16th centuries. The bibliography has almost 100 titles.

29
Bartlett, Richard A. Great surveys of the American West. Norman, University of Oklahoma Press [1962] 408 p. illus., maps. (The American exploration and travel series [38])   F594.B28

Bibliography: p. 377-390.

About the surveys conducted in the 19th century under the leadership of Frémont, Hayden, King, Powell, and Wheeler.

30
Bassett, Douglas A. A source-book of geological, geomorphological and soil maps for Wales and the Welsh Borders (1800-1966). [Cardiff] Amgueddfa Genedlaethol Cymru (National Museum of Wales), 1967. 239 p.

Z6026.G3B35

Bibliography: p. [195-211]

This volume "includes a summary of the evolution of geological, geomorphological and pedological cartography, with extensive notes on the sources of information; and contains comprehensive lists and indexes of the maps of Wales and the Borders."

31
Baughman, Robert W. Kansas in maps. Topeka, Kansas State Historical Society, 1961. 104 p. illus., maps.   G1455.B3 1961 G&M

"As a contribution to the Kansas centennial I am proud to publish a book that points to the wealth of Kansas maps and the fascinating story they have recorded through the centuries.... This book is not intended to be all-inclusive but only to show how the main facets of Kansas history are reflected in our astonishing variety of maps."—Foreword. The maps described and illustrated range in date from the 16th to the 20th centuries. They are not individually listed in cartobibliographic form but are described in an historical essay.

32
Baynton-Williams, Roger. Investing in maps. New York, C. N. Potter [1969] 160 p. illus., maps.   GA300.B3

Also published in London by Barrie & Rockliff, the Cresset P., 1969.

GA300.B3 1969b

"In the context of this book ... the word 'investing' means buying old maps wisely, that the purchaser should have some fundamental knowledge of map collecting which will assist him to make a decision and to ensure that any capital outlay money is well spent." Includes many illustrations and maps, some in color.

33

Beans, George H. A list of Japanese maps of the Tokugawa era. Jenkintown [Pa.] Tall Tree Library, 1951. 51 p. maps. (Tall Tree Library publication no. 23)   Z6027.J24B4

– – – – – – Supplements A-C. 1955-63. (Tall Tree Library publications no. 24-26) 3 v. illus., maps.   Z6027.J24B4s suppl. A-C

The Tokugawa Era began in 1615 and ended in 1867. "Japanese maps of the sixteenth century or earlier are too rare; after 1867 they become too plentiful. . . . The present compilation will, it is hoped, be helpful to others who may care to study old Japanese maps." In the bibliography "attention is called to helpful studies of some of the problems which we here can merely mention casually." There are a number of collotype reproductions of maps.

34

Beazley, Charles R. The dawn of modern geography . . . A history of exploration and geographical science . . . with reproductions of the principal maps of the time. London, J. Murray [1905?]-06. 3 v. illus., maps.   G89.B38 1905

Contents.– v.1. From the conversion of the Roman Empire to A.D. 900, with an account of the achievement and writings of the Christian, Arab, and Chinese travellers and students.– v. 2. From the close of the ninth to the middle of the thirteenth century (A.D. 900-1260).– v. 3. From the middle of the thirteenth century to the early years of the fifteenth century (A.D. 1260-1420).

Reprinted in New York by P. Smith, 1949.

An extensive work on medieval geography covering the period from A.D. 300 to 1420, with emphasis on the history of discovery and exploration. Each volume contains a section of maps for the period covered.

35

Becker, Robert H. Diseños of California ranchos; maps of thirty-seven land grants, 1822-1846, from the records of the United States District Court, San Francisco. San Francisco, Book Club of California, 1964. unpaged, maps.
                                                                          HD211.C2B4

There are facsimile maps, in color, of the 37 diseños.

36

Bedini, Silvio A. Early American scientific instruments and their makers. Washington, Museum of History and Technology, Smithsonian Institution, U.S. Govt. Print. Off., 1964. 184 p. illus. (U.S. National Museum Bulletin 231)
                                                                       Q11.U6 No. 231

Bibliography: p. 172-176.

Includes illustrations of early surveying instruments and references to surveyors, cartographers, and globemakers.

37

Bell, James Ford. Jesuit relations, and other Americana in the library of James F. Bell; a catalogue compiled by Frank K. Walter and Virginia Doneghy. Minneapolis, University of Minnesota Press [1950] 419 p.   Z1203.B4

"The James F. Bell collection of Americana . . . consists primarily of fundamental accounts of the discoveries of America, the later discoveries and explorations of eastern and central Canada, the Red and Upper Mississippi Valleys, and the Great Lakes region adjacent to them, and the voyages and expeditions in search of a Northwest Passage to the Pacific Ocean by way of Hudson Bay."–Foreword. The items, which include a number of cartographical interest, are arranged chronologically. There is an alphabetical index. See item 224 for a "list of additions" to the collection.

38

Berlin. Ibero-amerikanisches Institut. Alexander von Humboldt und seine Welt. 1769-1859. [Ausstellung,] Ibero-amerikanisches Institut, Preussischer Kulturbesitz. Schloss Charlottenburg, Orangerie, Berlin, 29. Juni bis 10. August 1969. (Katalog: Peter Hahlbrock. Berlin. Preussischer Kulturbesitz, Iberoamerikanisches Institut, 1969) 109 p. illus.   Q143.H9B52

A catalog of an exhibit commemorating the 200th anniversary of Humboldt's birth. Includes many illustrations.

39

Bern (Canton). Kantonale Kartographiekommission. Landesvermessung und Kartographie des Kantons Bern. [Part 2] Kantonaler Karten- und Plankatalog, Bern. Bearb. von Georges Grosjean. Bern, Staatlicher Lehrmittelverlag, 1960- 534 p.   Z6027.B36A52

Lists all types of maps and charts in various Swiss libraries and archives that relate to the territory embraced by the Canton Bern to 1800. There are 5,112 annotated titles in a classed arrangement, with an alphabetical index.

40

Berwick, Jacobo María del Pilar Carlos Manuel Stuart Fitz-James, 10. duque de, ed. Mapas españoles de América, siglos XV-XVII. Madrid, 1951. 351 p. maps.   G1100.B4 G&M

Issued in portfolio.

An auxiliary work to the study of the cartographical development of North and South America from the 15th to the 17th centuries. Each of the maps reproduced is followed by extensive annotations including descriptions, lists of names on the maps, and bibliographical references. Magnificently produced.

41

Bibliotheca cartographica. 1957- Bibliography of the cartographical literature. Semi-annual. Bad Godesberg, Bundesanstalt für Landeskunde (Germany.

Federal Republic) in cooperation with the Deutsche Gesellschaft für Kartographie, Z6021.B55

An international classified bibliography of cartographical literature. Includes a section on the history of cartography, subdivided into general history, regional history, and biography and personal data. Through 1971, 28 numbers had been issued. The current editors are Karl-Heinz Meine, H. Kramm, and R. D. Schmidt.

42
Blewitt, Mary. Surveys of the seas; a brief history of British hydrography. Foreword by Archibald Day; appendix on ships and instruments by G. P. B. Naish. [London] Macgibbon & Kee [1957] 168 p. illus., maps.

VK597.G72B5

Based on selections from the manuscript records in the British Admiralty Hydrographic Department. Includes reproductions of many early charts.

43
Blondeau, R. A. Mandarijn en astronoom. Ferdinand Verbiest, s.j. (1623-1688) aan het hof van de Chinese keizer. Utrecht, Desclée de Brouwer [1970] 525 p. QB36.V46B55

Biography, bibliography, and works of Ferdinand Verbiest, the Dutch cartographer who spent most of his life in China. In Dutch.

44
Blumer, Walter. Die topographischen Karten des Kantons Glarus. Einsiedeln, In Kommission bei Benziger, 1950. 44 p. (Schweizerischer Kartenkatalog, Faszikel 1) Z6027.G55B5

Bibliography: p. [40]

ʳ This publication traces the evolution of the presentation of topography on maps of Glarus, Switzerland, dating back to 1496. There are reproductions of portions of a number of the maps that are described in the text.

45
Bonacker, Wilhelm. Grundriss der fränkischen Kartographie des 16. und 17. Jahrhunderts. Würzburg, Freunde Mainfränkischer Kunst und Geschichte; Auslieferung: Buchdr. K. Hart, Volkach vor Würzburg, 1959. 78 p. illus. (Mainfränkische Hefte, Heft 33) GA875.F7B6

Cartography of the Mainfränkischer (Franconia) region of Germany in the 16th and 17th centuries.

46
— — Kartenmacher aller Länder und Zeiten. Stuttgart, H. Hiersemann, 1966. 243 p. Z6021.B69

Introductory text is given in German and in English. The work is "a compilation of the most important map-makers of all tongues and periods." In addition to mapmakers, it includes persons, past and present, "engaged in the production, publication and distribution of maps and charts, namely, form-cutters, copperplate-engravers, carto-lithographers, map-drawers, publishers, printers and map-sellers. Furthermore, collectors, map-historians and bibliographers are included too." The compiler summarizes previously published compilations of this type, which are cited in footnote references. Each name in the list is written in the original form of the cartographer's native country; variants are given as cross-references. Bibliographic references are listed for specific mapmakers. "Anyone who sets out to compile such a list of map-makers for the whole globe must be conscious that it will need later corrections and supplements." The list includes 6,350 mapmakers.

47
– – – On forms for the planning and execution of research-work in the history of cartography. Imago Mundi, v. 18, 1964: 84-86.   GA1.I6

The article is based on an analysis of a questionnaire, distributed by the German Cartographic Society, which was designed to stimulate and guide studies in the history of cartography. "These forms contain everything that will contribute to the initial elucidation of a map or an atlas."

48
– – – Das Schrifttum zur Globenkunde. Leiden, E. J. Brill, 1960. 58 p.
                                                      Z6026.G6B6

"Sonderdruck aus Janus; revue internationale de l'histoire des sciences, de la médicine, de la pharmacie et de la technique, vol. 48, 1959."

A list of 660 references about globes and their history, with an author index. The entries are arranged chronologically, within century divisions.

49
Bonasera, Francesco. Forma veteris urbis Ferrariae; contributo allo studio delle antiche rappresentazioni cartografiche della citta di Ferrara. Firenze, L. S. Olschki, 1965. 105 p. maps.   Z6027.I8B6

A catalog of 66 maps of the city of Ferrara that date from 1605 to 1895.

50
Boston. *Engineering Dept*. List of maps of Boston published between 1600 and 1903, copies of which are to be found in the possession of the city of Boston or other collectors of the same . . . Feb. 1, 1903. Boston, Municipal printing office, 1903. 248 p. "Reprint of Appendix I, Annual report of the City engineer, Feb. 1. 1903."   Z6027.B8B91

– – – List of maps of Boston published subsequent to 1600, copies of which are to be found in the possession of the city of Boston or other collectors of the same . . . Feb. 1, 1904. Boston, Municipal printing office, 1904. 97 p. "Reprint of appendix J, Annual report of the city engineer [Feb. 1, 1904]. A supplementary list of appendix I . . ."   Z6027.B8B9

In the Library of Congress copy, both appendixes are in one bound volume. The maps are arranged chronologically within each appendix. Annotations supplement the descriptions, and locations of copies are indicated.

51
Bramsen, Bo. Gamle Danmarkskort; en historisk oversigt med bibliografiske noter for perioden 1570-1770. København, Politikens forlag, 1952. 159 p. illus., maps.   GA961.B7

A comprehensive cartographic history of Denmark for the period covered, with more than 140 reproductions, some in color. Useful also as a supplemental work on general cartographic history, as it includes brief biographical sketches of many of the leading cartographers of the 16th to the 18th centuries.

52
Bratt, Einar. En krönika om kartor över Sverige. Stockholm, Generalstabens lithografiska anstalt, 1958. 131 p. illus., maps.   GA991.B7

A historical essay on the cartography of Sweden with a number of facsimiles, some of which are in color. Covers the development and evolution of maps of Sweden from the earliest time to modern official cartography. Text is in Swedish.

53
Brazil. *Diretoria do Serviço Geográfico do Exército. Mapoteca.* Catálogo das cartas históricas da Mapoteca da Diretoria do Serviço Geográfico do Exército. [Rio de Janeiro] Impr. Militar, 1953. 230 p.   Z6028.B8

Catalog of the historic maps in the collection. There are 1,474 annotated titles in the list, dated principally in the 18th and 19th centuries. See also item number 120.

54
Brazil. *Ministério das Relações Exteriores. Mapoteca.* Catalogo da Mappotheca . . . Rio de Janeiro, Imprensa nacional, 1926-29. 2 v.   Z6028.B82

Contents.—pt. 1. Limites do Brasil.—pt. 2. Planispherios, atlas, Europa, Novo Continente, America meridional, Brasil, series hydrographicas.

Map catalog of the Mapoteca of Brazil's Foreign Office. The titles are arranged by geographical and administrative areas.

55
— — — Catálogo de plantas e mapas da cidade do Rio de Janeiro. [Elaborado por Isa Adonias, com a colaboração de Marta M. Gon[alves e Yolette Soares de Miranda. Rio de Janeiro] Seção de Publicações, 1966. 171 p. Z6027.R5B7

A list of more than 200 maps of Rio de Janeiro dating from 1558 to 1964, with a classified index.

56

— — — Mapas e planos manuscritos relativos ao Brasil colonial conservados no Ministério das Relações Exteriores e descritos por Isa Adonias para as comemorações do quinto centenário da morte do Infante dom Henrique. [I] Texto. [II] Mapas. [Rio de Janeiro] Ministério das Relações Exteriores, Serviço de Documentação, 1960. 692 p. illus.   Z6027.B82A54

This list of 824 manuscript maps relating to the colonial period of Brazil was compiled in commemoration of the fifth centenary of the death of Prince Henry the Navigator. The items are arranged by regions, chronologically within regions, and indexed. There are 10 reproductions of distinctive maps. The maps described are in the collection of the Mapoteca, in Brazil's Foreign Office.

57

Bricker, Charles. Landmarks of mapmaking; an illustrated survey of maps and mapmakers. Maps chosen and displayed by R. V. Tooley; text written by Charles Bricker; preface by Gerald Roe Crone. Amsterdam, Elsevier, 1968. 220 p. illus.   GA201.B74

Bibliography: p. 269.

Also published in London by Thames and Hudson, 1969, under the title: A history of cartography: 2500 years of maps and mapmakers.

"This book is about those old maps that fascinate collectors—and certainly, most of us."—Introduction. The text is a concise history of cartography. There are numerous illustrations and reproductions of old maps, many in color.

58

British Museum. *Dept. of Manuscripts.* Catalogue of the manuscript maps, charts, and plans, and of the topographical drawings in the British Museum. London, Printed by order of the Trustees, 1844-61. 3 v.   Z6621.B87M3

— — — — — — Another issue [c1962] Reproduced photographically by Gregg Associates, Brussels, from an original annotated edition.
                           Z6621.B87M3 1962a

"These volumes contain a description of the whole of the Maps, Charts, Plans and Topographical Drawings deposited in the Department of Manuscripts, together with those attached to the Library of King George the Third, and the Collections preserved in the Print Room."

59

British Museum. *Dept. of Printed Books. Map Room.* Catalogue of printed maps, charts and plans. Photolithographic edition complete to 1964. London, British Museum, 1967. 15 v.   Z6028.B863 1967

A comprehensive index to the maps in the British Museum, arranged in one alphabetical sequence by author and subject. The introduction includes information on the scope, character, and arrangement of the map catalogue. It "contains entries for (a) maps, atlases, globes and related materials including literature on them preserved in the Map Room . . . and (b) the more important cartographic materials in other collections of the Department of Printed Books and of Oriental Printed Books and Manuscripts." A major cartobibliographic reference aid.

— — — — — — Exerpt. World: an excerpt from the British Museum catalogue of printed maps, charts and plans. Photolithographic edition to 1964. London, British Museum, 1967. [237] p.   Z6028.B8602

A list of the world maps in the British Museum, excerpted from the *Catalogue of Printed Maps.*

60
Brown, Lloyd A. Early maps of the Ohio Valley; a selection of maps, plans, and views made by Indians and colonials from 1673 to 1783. [Pittsburgh] University of Pittsburgh Press [c1959] 132 p. illus., maps.   GA444.B7

"Description of the Maps": p. 69-127.
Bibliography: p. 128-132.

"This book is primarily a picture book containing a brief review and summary of the cartographic record left by the men who first explored and mapped the region of the Ohio."

61
— — — The story of maps. Boston, Little, Brown, 1949. 397 p. illus., maps.
GA201.B76 1949

Bibliography: p. [341]-373.

A general introduction to the history of mapmaking, with more emphasis on the development of techniques than on exploration and discovery. Includes an extensive bibliography.

62
Brown University. *John Carter Brown Library.* A collection's progress: two retrospective exhibitions. Providence, Associates of the John Carter Brown Library, 1968. 79 p. illus., maps.   Z1207.B872

Supplements the library's catalog of an exhibition held in 1949: In retrospect, 1923-1949.
Catalog of two exhibitions: one held at the Grolier Club, New York City, Apr. 16-June 1, 1968; the other at the library, Providence, Apr. 5-Sept. 1, 1968.

The two exhibitions included a number of cartographic items, which are described in the catalog.

63
Buenos Aires. Biblioteca Nacional. Catálogo de la mapoteca. Prólogo de M. Selva. Buenos Aires, Impr. de la Biblioteca Nacional, 1941-56. 2 v.

Z6028.B94

Contents—1. pt. Mapas.—2. pt. Mapas argentinos.

Catalog of the map collections in the Argentine National Library. Both parts include introductions by Manuel Selva, curator of the map collections. Part 1 has 182 titles; entries in part 2 are unnumbered. Both volumes have alphabetical indexes.

64
Bunbury, *Sir* Edward Herbert. A history of ancient geography among the Greeks and Romans, from the earliest ages till the fall of the Roman Empire. With a new introduction by W. H. Stahl. 2d ed. New York, Dover Publications [1959] 2 v. maps.   G84.B95 1959

A source book containing information about the world, nations, and peoples known to the Greeks and Romans. It contains many references to ancient Greek maps.

65
Burrus, Ernest J. Kino and the cartography of northwestern New Spain. [Tucson] Arizona Pioneers' Historical Society, 1965. 104 p. illus., maps.

GA407.K5B8

Bibliography: p. 77-84.

About a late 17th- and early 18th-century explorer and mapmaker in Spanish America (i.e., southwestern and western United States). The book includes a "brief sketch of [Eusebio Francisco] Kino's life, a list of his maps and charts, an outline of the pre-Kino geography of northwestern New Spain, his principal cartographical contributions, and . . . a few references to the abiding influence of his maps."

66
California. University. *Bancroft Library.* Index to printed maps. Boston, G. K. Hall, 1964. 521 p.   Z6028.C17

Photo-offset reproductions of more than 1,000 catalog cards, arranged alphabetically, that describe maps in the Bancroft Library. A brief introduction gives background information about the library. The *Index* is not "a collection of histories, but rather a collection of source materials for research and the writing of history."

67
Campbell, Tony. New light on the Jansson-Visscher maps of New England. London, Map Collectors' Circle, 1965. 20 p. illus., maps. (Map Collectors' Circle. Map collectors' series, no. 24)   Z6003.M3, no. 24

An analytical study of some 28 variants of this significant 17th-century map of a portion of the North American continent.

68

Canada. *Public Archives.* Sixteenth-century maps relating to Canada; a check-list and bibliography. Compiled by the Map Division. Ottawa, 1956 [i.e. 1957] 283 p.   Z6027.C22C3

"This check-list is a by-product of the effort made by the Public Archives . . . to expand its study collection of reproductions of early maps relating to Canada. As no adequate guide to 16th century maps was available, the Map Division began to compile lists for its own use." The volume contains an introduction to early Canadian cartography by T. E. Layng, lists of Agnese atlases and Italian atlases of the 16th century, a comprehensive bibliography, and an index. Describes 830 maps.

69

Chapin, Edward L., *Jr.* A selected bibliography of southern California maps, with a foreword by Clifford H. MacFadden. Berkeley, University of California Press, 1953. 124 p. map.   Z6027.C15C5

"The desire to make the great variety of maps of southern California available to persons in need of them has been the major purpose of this work." The emphasis is on physical and resource maps. The 624 maps "are arranged by the size of area covered and by date," within subject categories.

70

Chubb, Thomas. The printed maps in the atlases of Great Britain and Ireland; a bibliography, 1579-1870 . . . with an introduction by F. P. Sprent . . . and biographical notes on the map makers, engravers and publishers by T. Chubb, assisted by J. W. Skells and H. Beharrell. With numerous reproductions . . . London, Homeland Association [1927] 479 p. illus., maps.   Z6027.G7C5

Contents.—1. Atlases of England and Wales.— 2. Scotland.— 3. Ireland.— 4. Biographical notes of mapmakers, engravers, and publishers, with a general index.

A comprehensive study giving descriptions and lists of maps, based primarily on the British Museum atlas collection. See also item 302.

71

Cincinnati. Public Library. *Rare Book Dept.* A checklist of books relating to the discovery, exploration, and description of America, from Columbus to Mackenzie, 1492-1801. Compiled by Yeatman Anderson III, Curator. [Cincinnati] Public Library of Cincinnati and Hamilton County, 1961. unpaged.   Z1212.C5

Includes bibliography.

There are 196 references in the checklist, many of them relating to early American cartography.

72
Cincinnati. Public Library. *Inland Rivers Library.* Catalog of the Inland Rivers
Library. Compiled by Clyde N. Bowden. With a foreword by Frederick Way,
Jr. "Based on the collection of the Sons and Daughters of Pioneer River-
men." Cincinnati, 1968. 156 p. illus.   G&M Div. Pamphlet File

"The catalog . . . is issued in order to make the contents of the collection
better known to those students and scholars interested in the history of
commercial navigation and the development of the steamboat in the Mississippi and Ohio valleys, with particular emphasis on the Ohio. The period
covered is from about 1800 to the present."—Bowden. Includes entries for
approximately 140 maps.

73
Claussen, Martin P., *and* Herman R. Friis. Descriptive catalog of maps published by Congress, 1817-1843. Washington, D.C., 1941. 104 p. Z6027.U5C6

"This is a catalog of the 503 maps that are scattered throughout volumes 1
to 429 of the 'Congressional Series,' the volumes containing the documents
published by the 15th through the 27th Congress, between 1817 and 1843."
The maps "are described in the order in which they physically appear in
the . . . Congressional Series." There is an alphabetical index. A revised and
expanded version of this catalog is in press.

74
Colles, Christopher. A survey of the roads of the United States of America,
1789. Edited by Walter W. Ristow. Cambridge, Belknap Press of Harvard
University Press, 1961. 227 p. illus., maps. (The John Harvard library)
GA407.C6R5

"Bibliography of Christopher Colles": p. 107.
Bibliography: p. 109-114.

There are facsimile reproductions of the 83 strip maps from this first
United States road atlas, as well as biographical and descriptive essays about
the author and the survey.

75
Comitato onoranze ad Amerigo Vespucci nel quinto centenario della nascita.
Mostra vespucciana. Catalogo. Firenze, Palazzo vecchio, giugno 1954- settem-
bre 1955. [Firenze, 1955] 188 p. illus., maps.   Z8940.C6

A bibliography of reference works relating to Amerigo Vespucci, compiled
in honor of the fifth centenary of his birth. It includes a list of 35 maps, a
number of which are reproduced at reduced scales.

76
Cortés, Vicenta. Catálogo de mapas de Colombia. Madrid, Ediciones Cultura
Hispánica, 1967. 337 p. illus.   Z6027.C67C58

Bibliography: p. 53-56.

A total of 653 maps relating to Colombia are described in a chronological arrangement. Twelve of the maps are reproduced at reduced scales.

77

Cortesão, Armando. Cartografia e cartógrafos portugueses dos séculos XV e XVI. (Contribuïção para um estudo completo) . . . Lisboa, Edição da "Seara nova," 1935. 2 v. illus., maps. GA1011.C6

An exhaustive study of Portuguese portolan charts and their makers, with many bibliographic references and an extensive index. Facsimiles of 46 charts are included. "The most important work, not only on early Portuguese cartography but on early cartography, published for many years" (*Imago Mundi,* v. 2, 1937, p. 98).

78

– – – History of Portuguese cartography. Lisboa, Junta de Investigações do Ultramar. 1969-71. (Agrupamento de Estudos de Cartografia Antiga. [Publicações] 6) GA1011.C62

Contents.–v. 1. From the earliest times to the fourteenth century.–v. 2. Fourteenth and fifteenth centuries, with two chapters on history of astronomical navigation, by Luis de Albuquerque.

Bibliography: v. 1, p. [307]-312.

Volume 1 was published in 1969, and volume 2 appeared in 1971; one more volume is promised. "I have . . . written this book not only for scholars or for the inner circle of academic specialists in the history of cartography but mainly for those who wish to be initiated into these studies, and above all FOR MY STUDENTS."

79

– – – The nautical chart of 1424 and the early discovery and cartographical representation of America; a study on the history of early navigation and cartography. With a foreword by Maximino Correia. [Coimbra] University of Coimbra, 1954. 123 p. illus., maps. GA369.C6

"Appearing also . . . [in Portuguese] in the Revista Portuguesa de história, published by the Faculty of Letters of [the University of Coimbra]."

Bibliography: p. 113-116.

An analytical study of a chart on parchment that shows an island named "Antilia" in the western Atlantic. The chart is now in the James Ford Bell collection, University of Minnesota Library.

80

Cortesão, Armando, *and* Avelino Teixeira da Mota. Portugaliae monumenta cartographica. Lisboa, 1960-[62] 6 v. illus., maps.
G1025.C6 1960 G&M Div.

Contents.—v. 1 [Earliest cartography to the middle of the 16th century] —v. 2 [Middle of the 16th century to the last decade] —v. 3 [Last part of the 16th century] —v. 4 [Chiefly 17th century] —v. 5 [17th century] —v. 6. Index.

Prepared to commemorate the fifth centenary of the death of Prince Henry the Navigator, this six-volume work constitutes one of the truly magnificent and monumental works on the history of cartography. A number of the reproductions are in color and the remainder are in sepia. The text is in Portuguese and English. The index volume includes a list of Portuguese cartographers earlier than the 18th century, with their works, as well as tables of contents for volumes 1-5.

81
Crone, Gerald Roe. Maps and their makers: an introduction to the history of cartography. 4th (rev.) ed. London, Hutchinson, 1968. 181 p. illus., maps. (Hutchinson university library. Geography)   GA201.C7 1968

    Bibliography: p. 172-179.

"A map can be considered from several aspects, as a scientific report, a historical document, a research tool, and an object of art. In this outline I have endeavoured to balance these considerations, and to regard maps as products of a number of processes and influences. . . . My aim has been to indicate the main stages of cartographic development to which many countries have contributed in turn." There is "in an appendix a list of the more important volumes of map reproductions." Revision and expansion of a book originally published in 1953 by Crone, former Librarian of the Royal Geographical Society.

82
Cumming, William Patterson. North Carolina in maps. Raleigh, State Dept. of Archives and History, 1966. 36 p. maps.   G1300.C8 1966 G&M Div.

    Consists of 15 facsimile maps of North Carolina, dated from 1585 to 1896, with explanatory text.

83
— — — The Southeast in early maps, with an annotated check list of printed and manuscript regional and local maps of southeastern North America during the colonial period. Chapel Hill, University of North Carolina Press [1962] 284 p. 67 maps.   GA405.C8 1962

"A study of the historical cartography of the southeastern region of North America before the American Revolution. It attempts to analyze the manuscript and printed maps of that area, showing the expansion of geographical knowledge through the periods of discovery and colonization, and at times relates these maps to other primary documents of the period. . . . The list of maps attempts to make an exhaustive check of all regional maps of the Southeast and of local maps south of Virginia and north of the Florida peninsula." A reprinting, with some slight revisions, of the 1958 edition published by Princeton University Press.

84

Dahlgren, Per Johan, *and* Herman Richter. Sveriges sjökarta. [Lund, H. Ohls-sons boktryckeri] 1944. 413 p. illus., maps. (Statens Sjöhistoriska Museum. Handlingar 1)　　　　　　　　　　　　　　　　　　　　　　GA991.D3

"Publikationer": p. 346-347.

A comprehensive history of Swedish cartography and of Sweden's hydro-graphic surveys. The volume includes biographies of the directors of the surveys from 1643 to 1943. There is an English summary.

85

Dainville, François de. La langage des géographes: termes, signes, couleurs des cartes anciennes, 1500-1800. Avec le concours de Françoise Grivot. Paris, A. et J. Picard, 1964. 384 p. illus., maps.　　　　　　　　　　GA231.D3

"Les sources": p. xiii-xvii.

A comprehensive glossary of geographic and cartographic symbols and terms, given in various languages, with emphasis on terms used on early maps. The arrangement is classified, with separate indexes of terms, abbrevia-tions, signs, and colors. Dainville has "attempted to assemble in this volume the terms that have been used by the authors of maps, including the termi-nology or vocabulary, letters, lines and figures with which they have attempted to represent conditions and features on the earth, including the use of colors to express reality and to facilitate understanding and compre-hension of the map."

86

Danckaert, Lisette. Plans et vues de dix-neuf villes belges. Catalogue de l'exposition. (Bruxelles, Bibliothèque Albert 1er, du 10 janvier au 18 février 1968). Bruxelles, Bibliothèque royale, 1968. 95 p. plates.　　　NA9209.D3

The catalog describes 107 city maps, 24 of which are shown in reduced facsimile.

87

Darlington, Ida, *and* James Howgego. Printed maps of London circa 1553-1850. With a foreword by R. A. Skelton. London, G. Philip [1964] 257 p. illus., maps.　　　　　　　　　　　　　　　　　　　　　Z6027.G7D3

Bibliography: p. [44]

The list includes 421 maps. The "General Introduction" (p. 1-43) is a summary history of the evolution and development of London and its car-tography. "All the maps are grouped under the date and author headings." The catalog is based mainly on the collections in the Guildhall and London County Council libraries and in the British Museum and is limited to printed maps which are focused on London. Alphabetical index.

88

Dawson, Llewellyn S. Memoirs of hydrography, including brief biographies of the principal officers who have served in H. M. Naval Surveying Service between the years 1750 and 1885. Eastbourne, H. W. Keay [1883]-1885. London, Cornmarket P., 1969. 2 v. in 1.   VK597.G72D27

Facsimile reprint of 1st ed. in 2 v., Eastbourne, Henry W. Keay, 1885.
VK597.G9D3

"The object aimed at has been, to produce in a condensed form, a work useful for hydrographic reference, and sufficiently matter of fact, for any amongst the naval surveyors of the past . . . for reference." Biographical sketches of hydrographers of various countries are included.

89

Day, Archibald. The Admiralty hydrographic service, 1795-1919. London, H. M. Stationery Office, 1967. 378 p. illus., maps.   VK597.G72D3

A summary history of the British Admiralty Hydrographic Service, by a former Hydrographer of the Navy. The author notes that it is "a continuation of Commander L. S. Dawson's 'Memoirs of Hydrography, 1750-1885'. . . ."

90

Denucé, Jean. Les origines de la cartographie portugaise et les cartes des Reinel. Ghent, E. van Goethem, 1908. 136 p. maps.   GA1011.D5

On the early cartographic history of Portugal, with particular reference to the contributions of Pedro and Jorge Reinel.

91

Destombes, Marcel. Les cartes de Lafréri et assimilées (1532-1586) du Département des Estampes de la Bibliothèque nationale. Nouvelles de L'Estampe, 1970, n. 5: 234-274; n. 8: 353-355.   NE1.N67

Includes an introduction, a list of 206 Lafréri and Lafréri-type maps and plans, geographic and author indexes, and a bibliography.

92

– – – Catalogue des cartes nautiques manuscrites sur parchemin, 1300-1700. Saigon, 1941-   Z6026.H9D45

5. Cartes hollandaises: la cartographie de la Compagnie des Indes orientales, 1593-1743.

A total of 272 charts, dating from 1593 to 1743, are described. There are four plates with reproductions of early charts.

93

De Vorsey, Louis. De Brahm's Report of the general survey in the southern district of North America. Edited and with an introduction by Louis De Vorsey, Jr. Columbia, S.C., University of South Carolina Press, 1971. 325 p.

In 1764 William De Brahm was appointed Surveyor General for the Southern Department of the British colonies in America by the British Board of Trade. This volume contains the edited report for his survey of what is now part of southeastern United States. The introduction includes a biographical sketch of De Brahm.

94

Dionne, Narcisse E. Inventaire chronologique des cartes, plans, atlas relatifs à la Nouvelle-France et à la province de Québec 1508-1908. v. 4. Québec, published by the author, 1909. 136 p.   Z1392.Q3D5 t. 4

Included in this volume are a brief introductory essay on the cartography of New France and 1,252 map entries, arranged chronologically.

95

Dürst-Rangger, Arthur. Peter Anich. (Ausstellung) November-Dezember 1966. [Illustriert] Innsbruck, Tiroler Landesmuseum Ferdinandeum (1966) 40 p. illus.   GA833.6.A7D8

Illustrated catalog of an exhibit, held at the museum, which honored the life and work of Peter Anich, a 17th-century Tirolean cartographer and globe maker.

96

Durand, Dana B. The Vienna-Klosterneuburg map corpus of the fifteenth century; a study in the transition from medieval to modern science. Leiden, E. J. Brill, 1952. 510 p. illus., maps.   GA221.D8

Bibliography: p. [290]-321.

A detailed treatment of the origins of German cartography in the 15th century.

97

Eckert, Max. Die Kartenwissenschaft; Forschungen und Grundlagen zu einer Kartographie als Wissenschaft. Berlin, W. de Gruyter, 1921-25. 2 v. illus., maps.   GA105.E3

A monumental work on most phases of the development of cartography, with a wealth of historical and bibliographical data.

98

Engelstad, Sigurd. Norge i kart gjennom 400 år. Med opplysninger om dem som utformet kartbildet. Oslo, J. W. Cappelens antikvariat, 1952. 112 p. (J. W. Cappelens antikvariat. Katalog nr. 15)   K6027.N8E5

Bibliography: p. 111-[112] .

"This is the first specialized catalogue of cartography published by a Norwegian antiquarian bookseller. Its task is first and foremost to show the development of the map of Norway from the oldest printed map to the present day." Included are sea charts and maps of the polar districts, an annotated bibliography with some 200 citations, and a list of 471 maps. The foreword has been translated into English.

99

Essex, *Eng. Record Office.* Catalogue of maps in the Essex Record Office, 1566-1855. Edited . . . by F. G. Emmison, with a foreword by E. Lynam. Chelmsford, Essex County Council, 1947. 106 p. (*Its* Publications, no. 3)

DA670.E7A17, no. 3

– – – – – – First supplement. Edited . . . by F. G. Emmison. Chelmsford, Essex County Council, 1952. 53 p. (*Its* Publications, no. 16)

DA670.E7A17, no. 16

– – – – – – Second supplement. Edited . . . by F. G. Emmison. Chelmsford, Essex County Council, 1964. 52 p. (*Its* Publications, no. 39)

DA670.E7A17, no. 39

"From this admirable catalogue much information can be gleaned about English estate surveyors as well as about their maps."–Foreword. Volume 1 contains reproductions, some in color, an introductory essay, and an alphabetical index in addition to the annotated list of maps. "The chief aim of the catalogue is to give clear and concise particulars of what the original map shows, and, to some extent, what it does not show . . . . The catalogue includes all manuscript maps of earlier date than 1840."–Emmison. Approximately 500 manuscript maps are in the Essex Record Office.

100

Evans, Geraint N. D. North American soldier, hydrographer, governor: the public careers of J. F. W. Des Barres, 1721-1824. New Haven, Yale University, 1965 [c1966] 305 p. map. A dissertation presented to the faculty of the Graduate School Yale University in candidacy for the degree of Doctor of Philosophy. Ann Arbor, Mich., University Microfilms, 1967. Produced by Microfilm-Xerography.   F1032.D47E85 1966a

Between 1764 and 1773, Des Barres surveyed the waters around the Maritime Provinces of Canada and directed the production of the *Atlantic Neptune* series which charted the coastal waters of eastern North America. This is a comprehensive biography of Des Barres with considerable emphasis on his cartographic activities.

101

Eytzinger, Michael von. Der älteste Reiseatlas der Welt (Itinerarium orbis Christiani) Hrsg. von J[osef] E[gon] Schuler. Vorwort von A. Fauser und T. Seifert. ([Faks.] Neudr.) Stuttgart, Schuler [1965] 267 p.

G1792.E8 1965 G&M Div.

23

The introduction to this facsimile edition gives background information about this earliest printed road atlas.

102

Fauser, Alois. Die Welt in Händen. Kurze Kulturgeschichte des Globus. Stuttgart, Schuler, 1967. 184 p.   GA260.F3

An excellent history of early globes and globemakers. Well illustrated, including photoreproductions of old globes, many in color.

103

Fauser, Alois, *and* Traudl Seifert. Ältere Erd- und Himmelsgloben in Bayern. Im Auftrag der Bayerischen Staatsbibliothek. Stuttgart, Schuler, 1964. 184 p. illus.   GA193.G4F3

Discusses early terrestrial and celestial globes in various Bavarian libraries, with a number of illustrations, some in color. There is a list of 246 globes.

104

Fel', Sergeĭ Efimovich. Kartografiı̆a Rossii XVIII veka [Eighteenth-century Russian cartography]. Moskva, Izd-vo Geodezicheskoi Lit-Ry, 1960. 226 p. illus.   GA933.6.A1F4

A summary of Russian cartographical history in the 18th century. In Russian.

105

Fielding, Mantle. American engravers upon copper and steel. Biographical sketches and check lists of engravers; a supplement to David McNeely Stauffer's American engravers. Philadelphia, 1917. 365 p.   NE505.F5

Includes names, biographical sketches, and a list of works of many map engravers. See also item number 315.

106

Fiorini, Matteo. Sfere terrestri e celesti di autore italiano oppure fatte o conservate in Italia. Roma, La Società geografica italiana, 1899. 502 p.
                                                                                    GA284.I7F3

A comprehensive listing of terrestrial and celestial globes published before 1800, with author, location, and chronological indexes.

107

Fischer, Theobald. Sammlung mittelalterlicher Welt- und Seekarten italienischen Ursprungs und aus italienischen bibliotheken und Archiven. Vienna, F. Ongania, 1886. 254 p.   GA221.F52

Summary of Italian map- and chart-making in the Middle Ages.

108

Fite, Emerson D., *and* Archibald Freeman. A book of old maps, delineating American history from the earliest days down to the close of the Revolutionary War. Cambridge, Harvard University Press, 1926. New York, Arno Press, 1969 [i.e., 1970] 299 p. maps.   G1025.F55 1926a

"Arno Press edition, including The Vinland map."
Includes bibliographies.

Also reprinted by Dover Publications [c1969].   G1025.F55 1926b
and GA405.F5 1969

A study of American cartographic development as reflected in some 75 carefully selected maps. The historical significance of each map reproduced in facsimile is well documented. The reproductions in all three editions are inferior to map facsimiles of recent date.

109

Fockema Andreae, Sybrandus J., *and* B. van 't Hoff. Geschiedenis der kartografie van Nederland, van den Romeinschen tijd tot het midden der 19de eeuw, door S. J. Fockema Andreae, met medewerking van B. van 't Hoff. With a summary in English. 's-Gravenhage, M. Nijhoff, 1947. 127 p. ports., maps.   GA901.F6

"Bronnen en litteratuur": p. 2-5.

The attention of the authors is "focused on the geographical representation of the Netherlands territory throughout the ages; they have tried to draw a general picture of this interesting and sometimes intricate course of events, and to put this picture upon its appropriate historical and cultural background." Included are biographical and bibliographical data.

110

Fondazione Scientifica Querini Stampalia, *Venice*. Catalogo del fondo cartografico queriniano, a cura di Giuseppe Mazariol. Venezia, Lombroso, 1959. 154 p.   Z6028.F65

A catalog of the 391 maps, plans, atlases, and globes in the collections of the Fondazione. There is an introductory essay about the Venetian engravers and printers of geographical maps. Authors are indexed alphabetically.

111

Fordham, *Sir* Herbert George. John Ogilby (1600-1676), his Britannia, and the British itineraries of the eighteenth century. London, Oxford University Press, 1925. p. [157]-178. illus., port.   Z6027.G7F58

"Reprinted . . . from the Transactions of the Bibliographical Society (the Library)," 4th series, v. 6, no. 2, 1925, p. [157]-178.
Z671.L69 4th ser., v. 6, no. 2

Ogilby's survey "is of particular and historical importance, as it displaced the old British mile of 2,428 yards, and it substituted for it the statute mile of 1,760 yards, thus effecting a revolution in customary measurements."

112
– – – Maps, their history, characteristics and uses ... 2d ed. Cambridge, Eng., University Press, 1927. 83 p.   GA105.F6 1927

This volume "embodies the history of map-production from the earliest times, from the point of view of both science and practice and from that equally of the continuous development of the graphic art as applied to the pictorial and technical representation of the earth's surface on paper or other suitable material."

113
– – – The road-books & itineraries of Great Britain 1570 to 1850. A catalogue with an introduction and a bibliography. Cambridge, Eng., University Press, 1924. 72 p.   Z6027.G7F62 1924

Revised from "Catalogue of the road-books and itineraries of Great Britain and Ireland to the year 1850." This edition does not include road-books of Ireland.

"I make up a catalogue, as complete and exhaustive as the materials available allow, of the original titles of the Road-books and Itineraries of Great Britain, setting out, in addition, all the numerous reprints, reissues and editions which are known to exist."

114
– – – The road-books & itineraries of Ireland, 1647-1850; a catalogue. Dublin, J. Falconer, 1923. 14 p.   Z6027.I7F7

Supplements his list of road-books of Great Britain.

115
– – – Studies in carto-bibliography, British and French, and in the bibliography of itineraries and road-books. London, Dawsons, 1969. 180 p. illus., maps.   Z6027.G7F72 1969

Bibliography: p. 169-174.

Reprint of the Clarendon Press ed., Oxford, 1914.   Z6027.G7F72

Includes selected papers by the author, reprinted from various sources.

116
France. *Armée. Service Géographique.* La carte de France, 1750-1898. Étude historique par le Colonel Berthaut, chef de la Section de cartographie. [Paris] Impr. du Service géographique, 1898-99. 2 v. illus., maps.
                                   GA862.B51

The most comprehensive work on the history of official French cartography, with much biographical data about the men who contributed to its development. Included are a chronology and an excellent general index.

117
France. *Centre National de la Recherche Scientifique*. Liste des globes terrestres et celestes anciens—anteriéurs à 1850—conservés dans les collections publiques de France, by Gabrielle Duprat. Paris, Centre National de la Recherche Scientifique, 1970. 42 l. (Recherche cooperative sur programme no. 172)   G&M Pamph. Coll.

Compiled under the direction of M. Edmond Pognon, Conservateur en Chef du Département des Cartes et Plans, Bibliothèque nationale. The list includes 231 globes, which are presented in author and chronological arrangements.

118
Friis, Herman Ralph, *ed.* The Pacific basin; a history of its geographical exploration, edited by Herman R. Friis. New York, American Geographical Society, 1967. 457 p. illus., maps. (American Geographical Society. Special Publication no. 38)   DU23.F7

Bibliography: p. 337-440.

"This book is an outgrowth of a symposium on 'Highlights of the History of Scientific Geographical Exploration in Relation to the Development of the Pacific Map,' held as part of the Tenth Pacific Science Congress meeting at the University of Hawaii in Honolulu, August 21 to September 6, 1961." The volume contains 15 separate papers, including R. A. Skelton's "Map compilation, production, and research in relation to geographical exploration."

119
Fúrlong Cárdiff, Guillermo. Cartografía histórica argentina; mapas, planos y diseños que se conservan en el Archivo General de la Nación. Buenos Aires, Comisión Nacional Ejecutiva de Homenaje al 150º Aniversario de la Revolución de Mayo, 1963 [i.e., 1964] 391 p.   Z6027.A6F8

There are descriptions of 940 maps, ranging in date from 1577 to 1841, from the collections of Argentina's Archivo General de la Nación.

120
Furtado, Sebastião da Silva. Estudo das cartas históricas da Mapoteca da DSG. Rio de Janeiro, Diretoria do Serviço Geográfico [1959] 103 p. illus., maps.   GA671.F8

A descriptive catalog of noteworthy historical maps (16th to 18th centuries) in collections of the Serviço Geográfico. See also item 53.

121
Ganong, William F. Crucial maps in the early cartography and place-nomenclature of the Atlantic coast of Canada. With an introduction, commentary, and map notes by Theodore E. Layng. [Toronto] University of

Toronto Press, in cooperation with the Royal Society of Canada [1964] 511 p. illus., maps. (Royal Society of Canada. Special Publications, 7)

GA475.A8G3

Includes nine papers by Ganong which were originally published in *Transactions of the Royal Society of Canada,* 3d ser., 1927-37. Introduction includes a biographical sketch of Ganong.

122

Garcie, Pierre, *called* Ferrande. The rutters of the sea: the sailing directions of Pierre Garcie . . . with facsimile reproductions, by D. W. Waters. New Haven, Yale University Press, 1967. 478 p. illus.   VK551.C8 1967

Bibliography: p. 469-473.

A study of the first English and French printed sailing directions, with facsimile reproductions. The early 16th-century "rutters," or sailing guides, were forerunners of the nautical atlases that were introduced toward the end of the century.

123

Geerz, F. Geschichte der geographischen Vermessungen und der Landkarten Nordalbingiens vom Ende des 15. Jahrhunderts bis zum Jahre 1859. Berlin, Commissionsdebit, 1859. 277 (i.e., 281) p.   GA875.S4G3

History of surveying and mapping in the region of the lower Rhine, including Schleswig-Holstein, and Denmark.

124

George, Wilma B. Animals and maps. Preface by Helen Wallis. Berkeley, University of California Press [1969] 235 p.   GA203.G4

Bibliography: p. [211]-220.

Also published in London by Secker & Warburg, 1969.   GA203.G4 1969

The book seeks to support the thesis that animals portrayed on ancient maps are zoogeographically significant. There are reproductions, in whole or in part, of a number of early maps.

125

Ghent. Rijksuniversiteit. *Bibliotheek.* Inventaris der kaarten en globes. Samengesteld door Greta Milis-Proost. Gent, 1967. 463 p. (Rijksuniversiteit te Gent. Centrale bibliotheek. Bijdragen tot de bibliotheekwetenschap, 3)

Z6028.G5

Catalog of maps and globes in the library of the Rijksuniversiteit, Ghent, Belgium. There are descriptions of 1,834 maps and five globes, and a general index.

126

Der Globusfreund. 1952- Wien, Coronelli-Weltbund der Globusfreunde.
Annual.   GA260.G55

Editor: 1952-61, Robert Haardt; 1962-, Ernst Bernleithner.

An annual serial publication devoted solely to the study of historical and
modern globes. Various issues include articles, illustrations, bibliographies,
and biographical sketches and notes.

127

Goetzmann, William H. Army exploration in the American West, 1803-1863.
New Haven, Yale University Press, 1959. 509 p. illus., maps. (Yale publications in American studies, 4)   F591.G6

"Bibliographical essay": p. 461-480.

"The aim of this study is to describe, analyze, and evaluate the role played
by the U.S. Army in exploring the trans-Mississippi West, and in particular
the role of the Topographical Engineers between the years 1838 and 1863."
Appendixes include (a) Roster of the Corps of Topographical Engineers, (b)
Note on mapping techniques, and (c) C. G. K. Warren's method of compiling
the map of 1857.

128

Gt. Brit. *Public Record Office.* Maps and plans in the Public Record Office.
v. 1, British Isles, c. 1410-1860. London, H. M. Stationery Off., 1967. 648 p.
                                                             Z6028.G767

"This volume, the first of several planned on the maps and plans in the
Public Record Office, has been compiled by many hands under the direction
of Mr. H. N. Blakiston." The maps are arranged in the volume in seven
regional groups.

129

Grob, Richard. Geschichte der schweizerischen Kartographie. Bern, Kümmerly
und Frey, 1941. 194 p. maps.   GA1021.G72

Issued also in part as thesis, Bern.

A brief survey of Switzerland's representation in ancient and medieval
cartography, followed by a more detailed description of the 16th, 17th, and
18th centuries when Swiss national cartography was very richly developed. It
includes a number of map reproductions and copious bibliographical footnotes.

130

Grosjean, Georges, *and* Rudolph Kinauer. Kartenkunst und Kartentechnik vom
Altertum bis zum Barock. [Von] Georges Grosjean [und] Rudolf Kinauer.
Bern, Stuttgart, Hallwag [1970] 144 p. illus., maps.   GA201.G75

A summary history of cartography up to the 19th century, with excellent
reproductions (some in color) of noteworthy landmark maps.

131
Guarnieri, Giuseppe Gino. Geografia e cartografia nautica nella loro evoluzione storica e scientifica (dalle origini al sistema mercatoriano corretto) Genova [Fratelli Pagano Tipografi Editori s.p. A] 1956. 170 p. illus.   VK145.G8

Includes bibliography.

Traces the development of nautical geography and cartography through the 17th century.

132
Guedes, Max Justo. Brasil—costa norte: cartografia portuguêsa vetustíssima. Ed. comemorativa do centenário da Flotilha do Amazonas, 1868-1968. Rio de Janeiro, Serviço de Documentação Geral da Marinha, 1968. 69 p. illus.
GA673.6.G8

A cartographic history of the northern coast of Brazil (Maranhão region), based upon early maps and documents in the Biblioteca Nacional de Rio de Janeiro. There are color reproductions of five maps. The text is in Portuguese.

133
Guthorn, Peter J. American maps and map makers of the Revolution. Monmouth Beach, N.J., Philip Freneau Press, 1966. 48 p. illus., maps.
GA405.5.G8

Includes brief biographical sketches of some 50 mapmakers associated with the American Revolutionary forces.

134
Haasbroek, N. D. Gemma Frisius, Tycho Brahe and Snellius and their triangulations. Delft, Rijkscommissie voor Geodesie [Delft, W. D. Meinema] 1968 [1969] 120 p. illus. (Publication of the Netherlands Geodetic Commission)
QB311.H3

Bibliography: p. 116-119.

Biographical summaries on Regnier Gemma Frisius, Tycho Brahe, and Willebrord Snellius, Dutch cartographers of the 16th and early 17th centuries.

135
Haifa. Maritime Museum. Old maps of the Land of Israel. Haifa, 1963. 57 p.
Z6027.I75H3

Maps of Israel, 85 in number, are described in this exhibit catalog. There are a number of reproductions, some in color, and a list of cartographers. Text is in Hebrew and English.

136

Hall, Tord. Carl Friedrich Gauss, a biography. Translated by Albert Froderberg. Cambridge, M. I. T. Press [1970] 175 p. QA29.G3H353

Translation of Gauss, matematikernas Konung.
Bibliography: p. [171]-[172]

Carl Friedrich Gauss, a distinguished mathematician, also worked in the fields of cartography and geodesy. His name is associated with several map projections.

137

Hammond, George P., *and* Dale L. Morgan. Captain Charles M. Weber: pioneer of the San Joaquin and founder of Stockton, California; with a description of his papers, maps, books . . . now in the Bancroft Library. Berkeley, Calif., Friends of the Bancroft Library, 1966. 118 p. illus., maps. (Friends of the Bancroft Library. General publication no. 1) Z8956.H3

"The collection of maps formed . . . by Charles M. Weber and his children . . . is one of the greatest cartographical archives ever created by a California family. . . . A considerable number of the maps are manuscript, and therefore unique. . . . A particular glory of the Weber collection is its wide variety of California maps of the 1850's."

138

Hapgood, Charles H. Maps of the ancient sea kings; evidence of advanced civilization in the ice age. Philadelphia, Chilton Books [1966] 315 p. illus., maps. GA300.H3
Bibliography: p. [292]-300.

"This book contains the story of the discovery of the first hard evidence that advanced people preceded all the peoples now known to history." The thesis of the book rests upon rather weak evidence.

139

Hargreaves, R. P. Maps of New Zealand appearing in British parliamentary papers. Dunedin, University of Otago Press, 1962. 24 p. map. (Hocken Library publication, no. 1) Z6027.N54H3

"Lists over seventy maps and plans dealing with New Zealand. . . . The New Zealand Parliamentary Papers . . . also contain many useful maps." Entries give date, scale, size, authority, and contents of the maps.

140

― ― ― Maps in New Zealand provincial council papers. Dunedin, University of Otago Press, 1964. 36 p. map. (Hocken Library publication, no. 2) Z6027.N54H28

Descriptions of 110 maps, with an alphabetical index. "Maps issued separately from council papers by provincial survey departments are not included in this bibliography.'

H̷ow, Neal. The maps of San Francisco Bay, from the Spanish discovery in 1769 to the American occupation. [San Francisco] Book Club of California, 1950. 140 p. maps.   GA413.H3

Bibliography: p. 127-140.

Thirty-nine maps, dating from 1771 to 1847, are described in a chronological arrangement, according to the date appearing on the face of the map. There are reproductions of a number of the maps. "Historical account of the explorations," "Notes to the historical account," "Notes to the maps," and a bibliography.

142
Harms, Hans. Künstler des Kartenbildes; Biographien und Porträts. Oldenburg, E. Völker [1962] 245 p. illus., maps.   GA198.H3

Includes a brief introductory history of early cartography and biographical sketches and portraits of some 100 early mapmakers.

143
Harrison, Fairfax. Landmarks of old Prince William; a study of origins in northern Virginia. With an introd. by John Melville Jennings. [Berryville, Va., Chesapeake Book Co., 1964] 2 v. in 1. 724 p. maps.   F229.H32 1964

Originally published in Richmond in 2 v., Priv. print, The Old Dominion Press, 1924.   F229.H32

Chapter 23 (p. 601-652), entitled "The Maps and Map Makers," summarizes the early cartography of Virginia.

144
Harrisse, Henry. Bibliotheca Americana vetustissima; a description of works relating to America, published between the years 1492 and 1551. Chicago, Argonaut, 1967. 199 p.   Z1202.H3 1967

A reprint of the 1866 New York edition of this classic reference work, together with its *Additions,* published in Paris in 1872. See also item 291.

145
— — — Découverte et évolution cartographique de Terre-Neuve et des pays circonvoisins, 1497-1501-1769. Ridgewood, N.J., Gregg Press [1968] 416 p. maps.   F1030.H32 1968b

Reprint of the edition published in London, 1900.   F1030.H32

A classic work on the early discoveries and explorations of the northeastern coast of North America.

32

146

– – – The discovery of North America; a critical, documentary, and historic investigation. With an essay on the early cartography of the New World, including descriptions of two hundred and fifty maps or globes existing or lost, constructed before the year 1536; to which are added a chronology of one hundred voyages westward, projected, attempted, or accomplished between 1431 and 1504; biographical accounts of the three hundred pilots who first crossed the Atlantic; and a copious list of the original names of American regions, towns and harbours. 802 p. maps. Reprinted, Amsterdam, N. Israel, 1961.   E101.H32 1961

Reprint of the 1892 ed. published in London by H. Stevens & Sons.

E101.H32

A most inclusive study of maps relating to early American history. It is a critical analysis of some 250 maps, many not previously recorded, including their nomenclature and characteristics.

147

Hart, Henry Hersch. Marco Polo, Venetian adventurer. Norman, University of Oklahoma Press [1967] 334 p.   G370.P9H28

Bibliography: p. 270-299.

"The author's concern has been to present the story of Messer Marco Polo as he has found it in the Venetian's own book, in contemporary chronicles, in later authoritative books and as a result of many visits and much personal research in Venice and elsewhere in Europe, America and Asia."–Preface. There is a section entitled "How Marco's book was first received, and its later influence on geography, cartography, and other sciences" (p. 258-262).

148

Harvard University. *Library*. A catalogue of the maps and charts in the Library of Harvard University in Cambridge, Massachusetts. Cambridge, E. W. Metcalf, 1831. 224 p.   Z6028.H33

V. 3, pt. 2 of "A catalogue of the library of Harvard University . . . 1830-31."

This catalog, "comprising as it does, the productions of all who have been most eminent in geographical delineations since the arrival of letters, . . . will be regarded as not the least valuable part of the general catalogue of the Library." Much of the collection was assembled by Prof. C. D. Ebeling of Hamburg. It includes many items pertinent to the early history of America.

149

Harvey, P. D. A., *and* Harry Thorpe. The printed maps of Warwickshire, 1576-1900. Warwick, Records and Museum Committee of the Warwickshire County Council, 1959. 279 p. maps. (Warwick County occasional series, v. 1)

GA795.W34H3

Bibliography: p. 253-255.

This book includes a descriptive introduction by Thorpe and a catalog, by Harvey, of some 140 maps.

150

Haskell, Daniel C., *ed.* Manhattan maps; a co-operative list. New York, New York Public Library, 1931. 128 p. map.   Z6027.N5H3

"Reprinted from the Bulletin of the New York public library of April-May & July-October 1930."

Lists maps in the New York Public Library, the American Geographical Society, the New-York Historical Society, and the Library of Congress. "This check list aims to enter maps of Manhattan Island and those maps of New York and vicinity which show the island in relation to the surrounding country. . . . The maps are arranged chronologically by date depicted." A total of 1,994 maps, ranging in date from 1600 to 1930, are described.

151

Hayes-McCoy, Gerard Anthony. Ulster and other Irish maps, c. 1600. Dublin, Stationery Off. for the Irish Manuscripts Commission, 1964. 36 p. maps.
                    G1830.H3 1964

This volume contains an introductory essay on early Irish cartography and 23 map reproductions (four in color), each with explanatory text.

152

Heawood, Edward. A history of geographical discovery in the seventeenth and eighteenth centuries. New York, Octagon Books, 1965. 475 p. illus., maps.
                    G97.H4 1965

Reprint of 1912 ed. published by Cambridge University Press.   G97.H4

Period covered "may be briefly characterized . . . as that in which, after the decline of Spain and Portugal, the main outlines of the world-maps were completed by their successors among the nations of Europe."

153

Heidel, William A. The frame of the ancient Greek maps, with a discussion of the discovery of the sphericity of the earth. New York, American Geographical Society, 1937. 141 p. (American Geographical Society, no. 20)
                    GA213.H4

"What seems to have distinguished even the earliest Greek maps, aside from their purpose to include the whole earth, is the frame enclosing the habitable earth. How this frame originated and was developed will be discussed in the pages that follow." The book is well documented with footnotes and is a good reference work on early Greek cartography.

154

Heissig, Walther. Mongolische Handschriften, Blockdrucke, Landkarten. Unter Mitarbeit von Klaus Sagaster. Wiesbaden, F. Steiner, 1961. 494 p. maps. (Verzeichnis der orientalischen Handschriften in Deutschland, Bd. 1)
                    Z6605.O7V4 Bd. 1

Bibliography: p. 451-453.

The items described are in various German libraries and archives. Section 2 (p. 335-446) describes Mongolian manuscript Landkarten, or maps, some 180 of which are listed. There are reproductions of several maps, a brief bibliography relating to Mongolian manuscripts, including maps, and an alphabetical index in the volume.

155

Hennig, Richard, *ed.* Terrae incognitae; eine Zusammenstellung und kritische Bewertung der wichtigsten vorkolumbischen Entdeckungsreisen an Hand der darüber vorliegenden Originalberichte. Leiden, E. J. Brill, 1944-56. 4 v.

G82.H42

Contents:—[1. bd.] Altertum bis Ptolemäus.—[2. bd.] 200-1200 n. Chr.—[3. bd.] 1200-1415 n. Chr.—[4. bd. 1416-97 n. Chr].

A reference work comprising critical evaluations of voyages and travels of discovery from earliest times to 1497. Name index in each volume.

156

Hensel, Werner. 75 [i.e., Fünfundsiebzig] Jahre Vermessungsamt der Stadt Düsseldorf. [n.p., 1960] 34 p. illus., maps. GA875.D8H4

On cover: Landeshauptstadt Düsseldorf.

A history of maps and plans of Düsseldorf, Germany, for the period 1885-1960. There are 23 map reproductions.

157

Historia de la cartografía; la tierra de papel. Organizada por José Aguilar. Buenos Aires, Editorial Codex, 1967. 239 p. illus., maps. (Georama: enciclopedia geográfica) GA201.H5

This Spanish-language book on the history of cartography is of particular interest because of its many color reproductions of historical maps. There are a general index, a list of illustrations, and an alphabetical list of authors and cartographers.

158

Hoffman, Bernard G. Cabot to Cartier; sources for a historical ethnography of northeastern North America, 1497-1550. [Toronto] University of Toronto Press [1961] 287 p. illus., maps. E121.H6

Bibliography: p. [229]-263.

There are separate chapters on the cartography of North America before Verrazano, and from Verrazano to Cartier, the cartography of the Cartier voyages, and the Homem cartography.

159
Huden, John C. Some early maps depicting the Lake Champlain area, 1542-1792. [Burlington, Vt.] 1959. 20 p. maps. ([Vermont. University] Monograph no. 2)   GA441.H8

Four of the essays in the pamphlet were originally published in *Vermont History* magazine.

160
Imago Mundi; a periodical review of early cartography. 1935- Amsterdam, N. Israel. Annual.   GA1.I6

Editors: Leo Bagrow (with Hans Wertheim, 1935; Edward Lynam, 1937-51); Leo Bagrow, 1952-59; E. Roukema, 1960; C. Koeman, 1962-71; Eila Campbell, 1972- ; publication suspended 1940-46, 1957-58.

A serial devoted exclusively to scholarly studies on the history of cartography. Twenty-five issues have been published through 1971. The papers are liberally illustrated, including many reproductions of early maps.

161
Imhof, Eduard. Die ältesten Schweizerkarten. Mit einem Faksimile der ältesten gedruckten Schweizerkarte von 1513. Zürich, Orell Füssli [1939] 15 p. maps.   GA1023.5.I5

Describes some of the earliest examples of Swiss cartography, largely from the 16th century.

162
[Inglis, Harry R. G.] The early maps of Scotland, with an account of the Ordnance Survey, by a committee of the Royal Scottish Geographical Society. 2d ed., rev. Edinburgh, Royal Scottish Geographical Society, 1936. 171 p. illus., maps.   Z6027.S42I5 1936
Bibliography: p. 149-155.

First edition published in 1934. "It has been the aim of the Committee to tap every available source, and although it is hardly possible now to recover some of the early maps and sketches of Scotland, it is hoped that the present collection will be found reasonably complete." There are a bibliography and an alphabetical index.

163
Instituto Historico e Geographico Brasileiro, *Rio de Janeiro. Bibliotheca.* Catalogo das cartas geographicas, hidrographicas, atlas, planos e vistas existentes na bibliotheca do Instituto historico, geographico e ethnographico brasileiro. Rio de Janeiro, Typ. Perseverança, 1885. 122 p.   Z6027.B82R5

The catalog describes 540 maps. There is an alphabetical author index.

164

International Bureau of the American Republics, *Washington, D.C.* A list of books, magazine articles, and maps relating to Central America, including the republics of Costa Rica, Guatemala, Honduras, Nicaragua, and Salvador, 1800-1900. Prepared by P. Lee Phillips... Comp. for the Bureau of the American republics. Washington, U.S. Govt. Print. Off., 1902. 109 p.   Z1437.B95

The list is arranged by Central America as a whole, then alphabetically by countries. Within each group there are lists of maps chronologically

165

International Geographical Union. *Commission on Early Maps.* Monumenta cartographica vetustioris aevi, A.D. 1200-1500. Catalogos paravit Commissio Cartarum Geographicarum Vetustiorum ab Unione Geographica Internationali mandata curantibus Roberto Almagià et Marcello Destombes. Monuments cartographiques anciens, A.D. 1200-1500. Catalogues préparés par la Commission des cartes anciennes de l'Union géographique internationale sous la direction de Roberto Almagià et Marcel Destombes. [Amsterdam, N. Israel, 1964-]   GA221.I48

In French
Includes bibliographies.

A comprehensive catalog of medieval mappae mundi, selected and compiled by an international commission of distinguished experts on the history of cartography. Other volumes in this series are to follow. There are 40 pages of illustrations and an index to the location of the manuscripts described, with approximately 130 citations.

166

— — — Rapport au XVIIe Congrès international, Washington, 1952, par R. Almagià, President de la Commission. [Paris] 1952. 2 v.

Fasc. 1, G56.I6 1952c
Fasc. 2, G&M Div.

Contents.—Fasc. 1: Contributions pour un catalogue des cartes manuscrites, 1200-1500, éditées par M. Destombes (p. 1-20); Macrobius, par M. Destombes (p. 21-33); Richard de Haldingham, par G. R. Crone (p. 34-37); Cartes catalanes du XIVe siècle, par M. Destombes (p. 38-63).—Fasc. 2: Catalogue des cartes gravées au XVe siècle, par Marcel Destombes.

The beginning of a comprehensive bibliography of all extant medieval maps, manuscript and printed, and portolan charts, of which the section on printed maps is complete.

167

Jackson, William Turrentine. Wagon roads west; a study of Federal road surveys and construction in the trans-Mississippi West, 1846-1869. With a foreword by William H. Goetzmann. New Haven, Yale University Press [1965, c1964] 422 p. (Yale Western Americana Series, 9)   HE356.A17J13 1965

Bibliography: p. 379-397.

A reprinting of a book originally published in 1952. "This study is an attempt to describe and assess the role of the federal government in the location, survey, and improvement of routes for wagons in the trans-Mississippi West before the railroad era."–Preface.

168
Jillson, Willard Rouse. A checklist of early maps of Kentucky (1673-1825). Frankfort, Ky., Roberts Print. Co., 1949. 27 p. illus., maps (*His* Transylvania series, no. 7)   Z6027.K4J5

"Outline of address delivered at Annual Meeting, Kentucky Historical Society, Frankfort, Kentucky, June 7, 1949." One hundred maps, dating from 1673 to 1825, are described.

169
Johnson, Hildegard Binder. Carta marina; world geography in Strassburg, 1525. Minneapolis, University of Minnesota Press [c1963] 159 p. maps.   G95.J6

"A publication from the James Ford Bell Collection in the University of Minnesota Library."

Comprehensive treatment of map publishing in Strassburg, Germany, around 1525, with particular focus on the works of Johannes Grüninger and Lorenz Fries.

170
Johnston, Frederick M. Knights and theodolites; a saga of surveyors. Sydney, Edwards and Shaw [1962?] 232 p. illus., maps.   GA85.J8

Distributed by Australian Book Center, New Rochelle, N.Y.

"This saga or cavalcade . . . deals with members of successive generations, each of whom was engaged in Western Australian land and survey operations. In addition to this family's uncommon historical background, facets of the profession of the land surveyor in a bygone horse or camel transport era are recorded nontechnically."

171
Jomard, Edme François. Introduction à l'Atlas des monuments de la géographie. Publiée par les soins et avec des remarques de E. Cortambert. Paris, A. Bertrand, 1879. 60 p.   GA205.J75

A summary history of cartographic evolution and development, prepared to accompany Jomard's noteworthy facsimile *Atlas des Monuments de la Géographie.*

172
Kammerer, Albert. La découverte de la Chine par les Portugais au XVIème siècle et la cartographie des portulans. Avec des notes de toponymie chinoise,

par Paul Pelliot. Leiden, E. J. Brill, 1944. 200 p. illus., maps. (T'oung pao; archives concernant l'histoire, les langues, la géographie, l'ethnographie et les arts de l'Asie orientale. Suppl. au v. 39)   DS740.5.P7K3

Part 2 (p. 179-216) is concerned with the early cartography of China, specifically portolan charts of this area. There are extensive footnote references.

173
– – – La découvert de Madagascar par les Portugais et la cartographie de l'île. Lisboa, Sociedade de Geografia de Lisboa, 1950. 113 p. illus.
                                                             DT469.M31K3

"Separata do Boletim da Sociedade de Geografia de Lisboa, nos. 9 e 10 da 67.ª série, setembro e outubro de 1949."

Includes a summary of the cartographical history of Madagascar for the period 1500-1667. There are black-and-white reproductions of several early maps.

174
Karpinski, Louis C. Bibliography of the printed maps of Michigan, 1804-1880, with a series of over one hundred reproductions of maps constituting an historical atlas of the Great Lakes and Michigan. Lansing, Michigan Historical Commission, 1931. 539 p. maps.   Z6027.M62K2

"In this work the attempt is made to give the list of all the printed maps of Michigan which appeared between 1805 and 1880 and also to indicate those earlier maps which were fundamental in the spread of information concerning the cartography of the Great Lakes." There are supplementary notes by William L. Jenks on "A Michigan Family of Mapmakers," "The Hutchins Map," and "Michigan Copyright." The list includes 1,000 maps.

175
Kartengeschichte und Kartenbearbeitung. Festschrift zum 80. Geburtstag von Wilhelm Bonacker . . . Hrsg. durch Karl-Heinz Meine. Bad Godesberg, Kirschbaum (1968). 261 p. illus.   GA108.K7
Bibliography of cartographic literature: p. 249-257.

Fifteen of the 30 papers in the Festschrift relate to the history of cartography. Eleven are in German, two in English, and one each in French and Dutch.

176
Kejlbo, Ib. Historisk kartografi. København, 1966. (Dansk Historisk Faellesforenings Håndbøger) 83 p.   GA201.K4

A brief Danish history of cartography, with emphasis on the Scandinavian countries. There is a classified bibliography of historical cartographical literature.

177
Kendall, Henry P. Early maps of Carolina and adjoining regions from the
collection of Henry P. Kendall . . . 2d ed., prepared by Louis C. Karpinski
. . . on the basis of the 1930 catalogue compiled by Priscilla Smith. [Charles-
ton, S.C., 1937] 67 p.   Z6027.C29K3

"Exhibited by the Carolina Art Association at The Gibbes Art Gallery,
Charleston, South Carolina, March 10-April 11, 1937."
Bibliography: p. 66-67.

Maps are arranged in three groups: (a) the world, the western hemisphere,
and North America; (b) English colonies and the United States; and (c, the
Carolina coast and the Carolinas. Some 323 maps are described with annotations. There is a brief bibliography of references on Carolina cartography.

178
Kimble, George H. T. Geography in the Middle Ages. New York, Russell &
Russell, 1968. 272 p. illus., maps.   G89.K5 1968

A reprint of the edition published by Methuen & Co., London, in 1938.

Includes a chapter (p. 181-204) on "Maps in the Middle Ages," which is a
good summary account of medieval mappae mundi.

179
Koeman, Cornelis. Atlantes Neerlandici. Bibliography of terrestrial, maritime
and celestial atlases and pilot books, published in the Netherlands up to
1880. Compiled and edited by C. Koeman. Amsterdam, Theatrum Orbis
Terrarum, 1967-71. 5 v. illus.   Z6028.K6

Contents.—v. 1. Vander Aa-Blaeu.—v. 2. Blussé-Mercator.—v. 3. Merula-
Zeegers.—v. 4. Celestial and maritime atlases and pilot books.—v. 5. Indexes.

A comprehensive catalog, including tables of contents, notes, and illustrations, of atlases published in the Netherlands between 1570 and 1880. "I
have set out to describe most of the maps by title, imprint, size and scale and
to indicate the major revisions and alterations of the plates in different
states."

180
— — — Collections of maps and atlases in the Netherlands: their history and
present state. Leiden, E. J. Brill, 1961. 301 p. illus. (Imago mundi; a review
of early cartography. Supplement 3)   GA193.N4K6 1961

Text and descriptions are in Dutch and English. "The scientific study of
the history of cartography has in the past been seriously hampered by our
limited knowledge of the source material and its whereabouts. The present
work is designed to remedy in part this situation and thus to contribute to
the improvement of the scientific foundations on which the study of early
cartography is built. This is to be achieved in three ways, viz.:
    1. by publishing a list of the map collections in the Netherlands at the
       present time;

2. by formulating a schematic outline of the bibliography of atlases published in the low countries before 1800;
3. by studying the character of map collecting throughout the centuries in general and by describing the history of Dutch map collections in particular.

The book attempts to give an over-all impression of the cartographic material at present existing in the Netherlands."

181

– – – The history of Abraham Ortelius and his Theatrum orbis terrarum. New York, American Elsevier Pub. Co. [1964] 64 p. illus., maps.

GA311 1570.O7K6

Issued to accompany a facsimile edition of Abraham Ortelius' 1570 *Theatrum.*

182

– – – The history of Lucas Janszoon Waghenaer and his "Spieghel der zeevaerdt." New York, American Elsevier Pub. Co. [1964] 72 p. illus., maps.

GA903.5.W25K6

Issued to accompany a facsimile edition of Waghenaer's 1584 *Spieghel.*

183

– – – Hanleiding voor de studie van de topografische kaarten van Nederland 1750-1850 [Guide to the study of topographical mapping in the Netherlands 1750-1850]. Groningen, J. B. Wolters, 1963. 120 p. illus., maps.

GA903.6.A1K6

The table of contents and the outline history, covering the period 1750-1850, are in Dutch and English. "My intention . . . is to bring the most important sources for the history of cartography of the Netherlands . . . within the reach of geographers, historians, surveyors, town- and county-planners and others who from time to time have to plunge into the study of early Dutch topography."

184

– – – Joan Blaeu and his grand atlas. Amsterdam, Theatrum Orbis Terrarum [1970] 133 p. illus.   GA315 1663.K6 1970

"Introduction to the facsimile edition of Le grand atlas, 1663."

Includes a biographical sketch of Blaeu and information about the Blaeu printing plant and the 12-volume *Le Grand Atlas,* 1663.

185

– – – Tabulae geographicae quibus Colonia Bonae Spei antiqua depingitur. Eighteenth-century cartography of Cape Colony. Amsterdam, Hollandsch-Afrikaansche Uitg. Mij., 1952. 64 p. maps.   G2563.C3L6 1952 G&M

41

The volume was published to commemorate the 300th anniversary of the first Dutch settlement on the Cape. A number of the reproductions are of manuscript maps. "This atlas presents a picture of the work done by Dutch surveyors when exploring the South African subcontinent." Title and text are in Afrikaans, Dutch, and English, and the title is given in Latin as well.

186

Kohl, Johann Georg. A descriptive catalog of those maps, charts and surveys relating to America, which are mentioned in vol. III of Hakluyt's great work. Washington, H. Polkinhorn, 1857. 86 p.   Z6027.A5K79

"In this treatise I will confine my researches to the American maps, because I have studied them a little better than those of the other parts of the world, and to the said 'third volume,' because in his other volumes and works Hakluyt has mentioned no American maps which are not at the same time mentioned in that.'

187

Kosack, Hans Peter, *and* Karl-Heinz Meine. Die Kartographie, 1943-1954; eine bibliographische Übersicht. Lahr-Schwarzwald, Astra [1955] 216 p.
                                                                                Z6021.K6

A general bibliography of references relating to cartography for the period indicated. There is a section on "Historical Cartography" (p. 27-39) which includes more than 350 titles subdivided under six headings.

188

Kraus, Hans Peter. Sir Francis Drake; a pictorial biography. With an historical introd. by David W. Waters & Richard Boulind and a detailed catalogue of the author's collection. Amsterdam, N. Israel, 1970. 240 p. illus.
                                                                          DA86.22.D7K73

Bibliography: p. 226-236.

"This presentation of the life of Sir Francis Drake in manuscripts, engraved portraits and views, maps, medals, and books, is intended to show him as he appeared to his contemporaries, both his own countrymen and his Spanish antagonists. . . . All this material is from the author's own collection."—Preface.

189

Kretschmer, Konrad. Die Entdeckung Amerika's in ihrer Bedeutung für die Geschichte des Weltbildes. Mit einem Atlas von 40 Tafeln in Farbendruck. Berlin, W. H. Kühl, 1892. 2 v.   E110.K92
Contents.—v. 1. Text, 471 p.—v. 2. Atlas, 40 maps.

Although this work commemorates the 400th anniversary of the discovery of America, it constitutes an excellent summary of historical maps in general from the earliest times to about 1520. The reproductions are, unfortunately, not true facsimiles, but redrawings.

190

– – – Die italienischen Portolane des Mittelalters; ein Beitrag zur Geschichte der Kartographie und Nautik. Hildesheim, G. Olms, 1962. 688 p. map. (Veröffentlichungen des Instituts für Meereskunde und des Geographischen Instituts an der Universität Berlin, Heft 13)   GA893.3K7 1962

A reprinting of a book originally published in 1909 by E. S. Mittler, Berlin.

A definitive study of portolan charts in general and of Italian portolan charts in particular. It includes descriptions of some 75 portolan charts and about 20 portolanos. It is most useful for names found on such charts and their modern equivalents.

191

Krüger, Herbert. Hessische Altstrassen des 16. und 17. Jahrhunderts, nach zeitgenössischen Itinerar- und Kartenwerken, 1500-1650. Kassel, Bärenreiter-Verlag, 1963. 119 p. maps. (Hessische Forschungen zur geschichtlichen Landes- und Volkskunde, Heft 5)   GA873.5.A1K7

Bibliography: p. 12-17.

About 16th- and early 17th-century roads and road maps of Hessen, Germany. There are a number of footnote references in each chapter.

192

Kubitschek, Wilhelm. Karten. In Pauly, A. F. von. Paulys real-encyclopädie der classischen Altertumswissenschaft; neue bearbeitung . . . Stuttgart, Metzler, 1919. v. 10, pt. 2, p. 2022-2149.   DE5.P33, v. 10

A comprehensive annotated list of ancient maps and globes, under the headings of city plans, Palestine, world maps by various authors, route maps, and globes, with numerous bibliographical references.

193

Kuchař, Karel. Early maps of Bohemia, Moravia, and Silesia. [Translated from the Czech original by Zdeněk Šafařík] Praha, 1961. 74 p.   GA841.K782

"The development of . . . ancient cartographic art found its contributors, among others, in the Czech Lands where a number of local inhabitants as well as foreigners . . . devoted themselves out of interest in their home or by official duty to the mapping of this part of Central Europe. This book is to describe their lives and activities, to appraise and to demonstrate their work." Several of the 12 plates are in color.

194

La Duca, Rosario. Cartografia della città di Palermo dalle origini al 1860. [Palermo] Banco di Sicilia, Fondazione per l'incremento economico, culturale e turistico della Sicilia "Ignazio Mormino" [1962] 173 p. maps.
GA895.P18L3

Descriptive list of 46 maps of Palermo up to 1860, with reproductions of a number of the maps.

195

La Guardia Trias, Rolando A. La aportación científica de Mallorquines y Portugueses a la cartografia náutica en los siglos XIV al XVI. [Madrid] Consejo Superior de Investigaciones Científicas, Instituto Histórico de Marina [1964] 72 p. illus., map. GA231.L3

A summary description of portolan charts, with numerous authoritative footnote references.

196

Lane-Poole, E. H. The discovery of Africa; a history of the exploration of Africa as reflected in the maps in the collection of the Rhodes-Livingstone Museum. Livingstone, Northern Rhodesia, Rhodes-Livingstone Museum, 1950. 28 p. illus. (The Occasional papers of the Rhodes-Livingstone Museum, new ser., no. 7) DT3.L33

Fifty-six maps, dating from 1478 to 1857, are listed with annotations.

197

Lang, Arend W. Seekarten der südlichen Nord- und Ostsee; ihre Entwicklung von den Anfängen bis zum Ende des 18. Jahrhunderts. Hamburg, Deutsches Hydrographisches Institut; Kommissionsverlag: Gebr. Borntraeger, Berlin, 1968. 105 p. illus., maps. (Ergänzungsheft zur Deutschen hydrographischen Zeitschrift, Reihe B, Nr. 10) GA370.L35

Bibliography: p. 102-105.

History of nautical charts of the Baltic and North Seas, with summaries in German, French, English, and Russian. Twenty reproductions of early charts.

198

Lauf, G. B. The origin and development of cartography; inaugural lecture delivered on 23 June, 1955. Johannesburg, Witwatersrand University Press, 1955. 34 p. GA201.L3

A summary history of the beginnings and evolution of maps and mapmaking.

199

Lee, Charles E. Introduction to facsimile edition of Atlas of South Carolina, 1825, by Robert Mills. Columbia, S.C., Wilkins & Keels, 1965.
G1305.M5 1965 G&M

The introduction includes biographical data about Mills and the story behind this first atlas of an individual state published in the United States.

200

Leithäuser, Joachim G. Mappae mundi; die geistige Eroberung der Welt. [Berlin] Safari-Verlag, 1958. 402 p. illus., maps. (Die Welt des Wissens)

GA300.L44

"Verzeichnis der Kartographen": p. 331-396.
Bibliography: p. 397-398.

A general history of cartography with a number of reproductions of early maps, several of which are in color. A revised, but unauthorized, version of Bagrow's *Geschichte der Kartographie* (item 23).

201

Lelewel, Joachim. Géographie du moyen âge. Bruxelles, V^e et J. Pilliet, 1850-52. 4 v. in 3. plates (part fold.), maps (part fold.) *and* atlas of 50 pl.

G89.L5

– – – Epilogue de la Géographie du moyen âge. Accompagné de huit planches. Bruxelles, V^e et J. Pilliet, 1857. 308 p. 4 fold. pl., 4 fold. maps.

G89.L5 Suppl.

Reprint of the 1852-57 edition by Meridian Publishing Co., Amsterdam, 1966-67. 5 v. in 3.

G89.L52

A comprehensive study of the Middle Ages, with a wealth of descriptive material relating to the maps of the Romans and Arabs.

202

Lenglet Dufresnoy, Nicolas. Catalogue des meilleures cartes géographiques. Générales et particulières. Avec quelques remarques sur la choix qu'on en doit faire. Amsterdam, Meridian Publishing Co., 1965 [1966] 252 p.

Z6022.L45 1966

"Rèimpression de la troisième de Méthode pour étudier la géographie, tome 1, seconde partie, Paris, 1742."

A reprint edition of an early list of cartographical works on maps.

203

Libault, André. Histoire de la cartographie. Paris, Chaix [1959?] 86 p. illus., maps.

GA201.L5

A popular history of cartography with a number of illustrations, some in color. A good introductory work for the layman who can read French.

204

Lister, Raymond. Antique maps and their cartographers. [Hamden, Conn.] Archon Books, 1970. 128 p. illus., maps.

GA205.L5 1970

Also published in London by G. Bell, 1970.

GA205.L5

Bibliography: p. 119-120.

A somewhat superficial general history of cartography. There are a number of black-and-white illustrations.

205
– – – How to identify old maps and globes, with a list of cartographers, engravers, publishers, and printers concerned with printed maps and globes from c.1500 to c.1850. Hamden, Conn., Archon Books [1965] 256 p.

GA201.L56

Bibliography: p. 109-115.

Also published in London by G. Bell [1965]   GA201.L56 1965a

Discussed are "An outline of the history of maps and charts," "Celestial maps and charts," "Methods of map reproduction," "Decoration and conventional signs," and "Terrestrial and celestial globes and armillary spheres." The appendix includes "the use of water marks in dating old maps and documents," a select bibliography, and "A list of cartographers, engravers, publishers and printers concerned with printed maps and globes from *circa* 1500 to *circa* 1850." There are 59 illustrations.

206
Łodyński, Marian, *ed*. Centralny katalog zbiorów kartograficznych w Polsce. Warszawa, Polska Akademia Nauk. Instytut Geografii, 1961-68. 4 v. in 3.

Z6028.L8

Contents–v. 1-2. Katalog atlasów i dzieł geograficznych, 1482-1800.–v. 3. Katalog atlasów, 1801-1919.–v. 4. Katalog atlasów i dzieł kartograficznych, 1528-1945.

The four parts include 2,743 titles of atlases and other geographical works ranging in date from 1482 to 1945. There are general alphabetical indexes, as well as indexes by subject, cartographers, publishers, and place of publication. The bibliography lists maps in the collections of the major libraries in Poland. This does "not fully correspond with the standards of a 'central catalogue'. It might be more appropriate to call this enterprise a large index of full catalogue descriptions based upon autopsies and kept in separate libraries as well as in the card catalogue of the Central Cartographical Catalogue."–Foreword, Stanisław Leszczycki. The arrangement of entries is by date within geographical or administrative areas.

207
Lowery, Woodbury. A descriptive list of maps of the Spanish possessions within the present limits of the United States, 1502-1820. Ed. with notes by Philip Lee Phillips. Washington, Govt. Print. Off., 1912. 567 p.

Z6021.A5U6

An annotated record of some 700 maps important in the history of North America, especially of the former Spanish colonies. It has extensive references to source materials as well as a comprehensive index. The collection has been in the Library of Congress since 1908.

208
Lübbecke, Fried. Das Antlitz der Staat; nach Frankfurts Plänen von Faber, Merian und Delkeskamp 1552-1864. Frankfurt a. M., W. Kramer, 1952. 156 p. illus., maps. DD901.F74L78

Includes biographical sketches of Friedrich Wilhelm Delkeskamp, Konrad Faber, Matthaeus Merian, and other early engravers of plans of Frankfurt.

209
Lunny, Robert M. Early maps of North America. Newark, New Jersey Historical Society, 1961. 48 p. maps. GA401.L8

Produced cooperatively by the New Jersey Historical Society and C. S. Hammond Map Company to commemorate the 60th anniversary of the latter. There are reduced-scale reproductions of 26 historical maps and brief descriptive notes. A concise summary of early American cartography.

210
Magnus, Olaus. Olaus Magnus Gothus. Ain kurze auslegung der neuuen mappen von den alten Goettenreich und andern Nordlenden. Venedig, 1539. Faksimile i ljustryck med inledning utg. af Isak Collijn. Stockholm, Cederquists grafiska aktiebolag, 1912. 22 p. GA954 1539

The facsimile of the map is 16 by 22 inches. The introduction, by Collijn, is in Swedish.

211
Map Collectors' Circle. Map collectors' series. no. 1- London, 1963- Z6003.M3
Irregular, 8-10 nos. a year.

"The aim . . . is to stimulate interest in and published material on early printed maps, atlases, cartographers, etc. . . . The emphasis [is] on material of practical importance designed to assist collectors, Librarians and Booksellers." Most issues are devoted to one topic, bibliography, or paper.

212
— — — North American city plans, being a selection of plans of the cities of Albany, Baltimore, Boston, Charlestown, Cincinnati, Detroit, Ebenezer, Montreal, Newport, New Orleans, New York, Philadelphia, Quebec, Savannah, St. Augustine and Washington. London, 1965. 12 p. illus. (*Its* Map collectors' series, no. 20) Z6003.M3 no. 20

"This number consists of a selection of 42 Town Plans of North America, all described and illustrated, ranging from the middle of the 16th Century to well into the 19th. Some 16 towns are noted."

213
Mariners' Museum, *Newport News, Va.* Catalog of maps, ships' papers and logbooks. Boston, G. K. Hall, 1964. 505 p. Z6836.M28

Reproduced by photo-offset from cards in the catalog of the Mariners' Museum. "There are approximately 5,800 cards in the map section. . . . The collection of over 1,600 maps is world-wide in coverage and dates from the early sixteenth century to the present time. Catalog entries for maps dated from 1500 to 1830 are arranged by date of publication; cards pertaining to modern reprints are filed according to the date of the original map."

214
Marks, Stephen Powys. The map of mid sixteenth century London; an investigation into the relationship between a copper-engraved map and its derivatives. [London] London Topographical Society, 1964. 27 p. maps. (London Topographical Society. Publication no. 100)   GA795.L6M3

"The purpose of this publication is to give a brief account of the most important maps depicting London shortly before and at the beginning of the reign of Elizabeth I and to show their relationship to one another."

215
Mathews, Edward Bennett. The maps and map-makers of Maryland, including a history of cartographic progress in Maryland. Baltimore, Johns Hopkins Press, 1898. 150 p. illus., maps. (Maryland Geological Survey. Special publication, volume II, part IIIb.)   Z6027.M3M41

Maps of the 17th, 18th, and 19th centuries are described and analyzed, and biographical material on a number of Maryland mapmakers is included.

216
Medina, José Toribio. Ensayo acerca de una mapoteca chilena. Introd. de Elías Almeyda Arroyo. Homenaje del Ejército de Chile a su autor en el centenario de su nacimiento, 1852-1952. [Santiago de Chile, 1952] 254 p.
                Z6027.C53M4 1952

– – – – – – Indice de autores y nombres [por] Carlos Stuardo Ortiz. [Santiago de Chile, 1952] 109 p.   Z6027.C53M4 1952 Index

Approximately 1,000 maps relating to Chile and the adjacent areas of the Pacific are arranged chronologically and described. The first volume contains a historical introduction.

217
Merian, Matthaeus. Die schönsten Städte Alt-Österreichs. Aus der Archontologia cosmica und den Topographien, mit einer Einleitung von Bruno Grimschitz. [Hamburg] Hoffmann und Campe [1963] xv p., illus., maps, 41 plates. (Merian-Bibliothek)   DB22.M4 1963

This is the third in the Merian-Bibliothek series "whose purpose it is to publish a selection from this unique work of that eminent engraver Matthaeus Merian (1593-1650)." This facsimile edition, which features cities of Austria, has a leaflet inside the rear cover which includes English translations of the captions for all plates. The introduction, in German, summarizes the life and work of Merian.

Meynen, Emil. International bibliography of the "Carte international du monde au millionième" (International map of the world on the millionth scale). (Bibliotheca cartographica. Sonderheft 1) Bad Godesberg, Bundesanstalt für Landeskunde und Raumforschung, 1962. 194 p. illus., maps.

Z6026.I8M4

Published "on the occasion of the United Nations Technical Conference on the International Map of the World on the Millionth Scale, Bonn (Federal Republic of Germany) August 1962." The bibliography provides "a historical review of the project and indicates the literature on the many related problems. . . . [It] also lists the reports on negotiations that were carried out at scientific and technical meetings." Index maps show coverage of the International World Map.

219

Michigan. University. *William L. Clements Library.* British headquarters maps and sketches used by Sir Henry Clinton while in command of the British forces operating in North America during the war for independence, 1775-1782. A descriptive list of the original manuscripts and printed documents now preserved in the William L. Clements Library at the University of Michigan, by Randolph G. Adams. Ann Arbor, The William L. Clements Library, 1928. 144 p.

Z6621.M63A2

There are 350 listings for maps, as well as three supplements and an alphabetical index. "The method of classification is geographical from north to south along the Atlantic seaboard of North America."

220

— — — Guide to the manuscript maps in the William L. Clements Library. Compiled by Christian Brun. Ann Arbor, University of Michigan, 1959. 209 p. maps.

Z6028.M5

"The purpose of this Guide is to list and briefly describe the manuscript maps contained in the Map Division of the William L. Clements Library. None of the many rare and valuable printed maps of early American history in the Division are included. These entries represent one part of the collection only." Some 806 maps are described. An appendix notes five collections, in other libraries, of which the Clements Library has photoreproductions. There is also an alphabetical index.

221

Milan. Civica raccolta delle stampe e dei disegni, *Castello sforzesco.* Le carte geografiche dell'Italia conservate nella Raccolta delle stampe e dei disegni; catalogo descrittivo [di Paolo Arrigoni e Achille Bertarelli] [Milano] Tip. del "Popolo d'Italia," 1930. [3]-424 p.

Z6027.I8M6

Catalog of 3,286 titles assembled by Achille Bertarelli from collections in the Civic Museum.

222

Miller, Konrad. Itineraria Romana, Römische Reisewege an der Hand der Tabula Peutingeriana. Dargestellt von Konrad Miller. Stuttgart, Strecker und Schröder, 1916. 992 p. illus., maps.　　　　　　　　　GA304.Z53M5

About Roman roads and road maps, i.e., the Peutinger Table.

223

– – – Mappae Arabicae, arabische Welt- und Länderkarten des 9.-13. Jahrhunderts in arabischer Urschrift, lateinischer Transkription und Übertragung in neuzeitliche Kartenskizzen. Mit einleitenden Texten hrsg. von Konrad Miller. Stuttgart, 1926-31. 6 v. in 3 portfolios. maps.　　　G1025.M49 1926 G&M

Issued in 14 parts.

The important link in the history of cartography formed by Arabic maps is the subject of this comprehensive survey, which emphasizes and ends with the contribution of Idrisi and his world map of 1154.

224

Minnesota. University. *Library. James Ford Bell Collection.* Antilia and America; a description of the 1424 nautical chart and the Waldseemüller globe map of 1507 in the James Ford Bell Collection at the University of Minnesota. [Minneapolis] 1955. 10 p. maps.　　　　　　　　GA369.M5

There is a reduced-size facsimile of the Antilia map, in color, folded inside the back cover.

225

– – – The James Ford Bell collection; a list of additions. Compiled by John Parker. Minneapolis, University of Minnesota Press, 1955-67. 3 v.

Z881.M6794

Contents.–v. 1, 1951-54 (1955), 69 p.–v. 2, 1955-59 (1961), 217 p.–v. 3, 1960-64 (1967), 207 p.

Additions published "as supplements to *Jesuit Relations and Other Americana in the Library of James F. Bell; a Catalogue,* by Frank K. Walter and Virginia Doneghy, published in 1950. . . . [see item 37] Acquisitions . . . emphasize the expansion of European commerce from the fifteenth to the end of the eighteenth century and . . . illustrate the close relationship between that commercial expansion and the growth of geographical knowledge." In general, Library of Congress cataloging practices are followed in the lists.

226

– – – Merchants & scholars; essays in the history of exploration and trade. Collected in memory of James Ford Bell, and edited by John Parker. Minneapolis, University of Minnesota Press [1965] 258 p.　　　　HF481.M55

Includes an introduction by the editor and 10 essays, by different authors, relating to early discovery, trade, and mapping.

227

Moir, Arthur Lowndes. The world map in Hereford Cathedral, by A. L. Moir; [and] , The pictures in the Hereford Mappa Mundi, by Malcolm Letts; with glossary and bibliography. 5th ed., rev. and rewritten. Hereford, The Cathedral, 1970. 40 p. illus., maps.   GA304.R5M6

Bibliography: p. 40.

Descriptive and analytical information about this famous mappa mundi.

228

Monteiro, Palmyra V. M. A catalogue of Latin American flat maps 1926-1964. Preface by Donald D. Brand. Austin, Institute of Latin American Studies, University of Texas [1967-69] 2 v. (Guides and bibliographies series, 2)
    Z6027.S72M6

Contents:—v. 1. Mexico, Central America, West Indies. 1967.—v. 2. South America, Falkland (Malvinas) Islands and the Guianas.

"This catalogue . . . is an attempt to partially fill the need that has existed since the American Geographical Society published *A Catalogue of Maps of Hispanic America*, . . . 1930-1932."—Preface. Arrangement is by subject within countries.

229

Morales Padrón, Francisco, *and* J. Llavador Mira. Mapas, planos y dibujos sobre Venezuela existentes en el Archivo General de Indias. [Sevilla] Escuela de Estudios Hispano-Americanos; [distribución exclusiva: Librería Científica Medinaceli, Madrid] 1964-65 [c1958] 2 v. illus., maps.   Z6027.V45M65

Contents.—[1. serie] Mapas. Planos. Varios.—[2. serie] Fortificaciones. Varios.

There are 150 entries in volume 1 and 152 in volume 2. Both volumes have indexes to the maps, as well as chronological, place, name, and document indexes. Both volumes include a number of black-and-white reproductions of maps and plans.

230

Morison, Samuel Eliot. The European discovery of North America; the northern voyages A.D. 500-1600. New York, Oxford University Press, 1971. 712 p.   E101.M85

Includes bibliographical references.

"The book here presented . . . is devoted to European voyages to North America prior to 1600. Together with a similar volume on the Southern Voyages to follow (God willing), it should replace John Fiske's classic *Discovery of America* (2 vols., 1893) and supplement an irreplaceable work, the first four volumes of Justin Winsor's *Narrative and Critical History of America* (1884-89). . . . The cartographical effort deserves special notice. Literary evidence of these early Northern Voyages must be supplemented by that of early maps showing bits and pieces of the New World. . . . Nobody has yet penetrated the secret of how the maps were made."—Foreword. An excellent, comprehensive review of a significant chapter in the history of discovery, exploration, and cartography. See item 388 for Winsor's *Narrative*.

231

Mota, Avelina Teixeira da. A cartografia antiga da Africa Central e a travessia entre Angola e Moçambique, 1500-1860. Lourenço Marques, Sociedade de Estudos de Moçambique, 1964. 225 p. maps.   GA1349.M6

  Bibliography: p. [247]-255.

A history of explorations and the development of cartography in central Africa up to 1860. There is a bibliography with some 130 references.

232

Muller (Frederik) en Compagnie, *Amsterdam*. Catalogue of books, maps, plates on America and of a remarkable collection of early voyages. With an alphabetical and a subject index by G. J. Brouwer, Librarian of the Dutch Booksellers Association Library. Amsterdam, N. Israel, 1966. 658 p.
                                                            Z1207.M95 1966

  Reprint of the 1872-75 Amsterdam edition.

Following the introductory essay on "Dutch-American Bibliography" are 2,288 titles.

233

Muris, Oswald, *and* Gert Saarmann. Der Globus im Wandel der Zeiten; eine Geschichte der Globen. Berlin, Columbus Verlag [1961] 287 p. illus., maps.
                                                            GA260.M8

  Bibliography: p. 271-276.

Designed to bridge the gap in information about early globes that was left between the publications of M. Fiorini (item 106) and E. L. Stevenson (item 317). A comprehensive treatment of globes and their evolution from the earliest extant examples to the present day. There is a reference list with more than 120 citations.

234

Nakamura, Hiroshi. East Asia in old maps. Tokyo, Centre for East Asian Cultural Studies; Honolulu, East West Center Press [1964, c1963] 84 p. illus., maps.   GA1081.N3 1964

An abridged English-language version of the author's "Tōa no Kochizu" (History of Mapping of the Eastern Asia) published in the *Journal of Yokohama Municipal University,* Series A-19, no. 88, March 1958. Principally concerned with maps and charts during the period of European exploration and colonization in East Asia. "The history of maps of East Asia outlined in this booklet may be said to be a history of 'maps seen from the ocean'."

235
— — — Maps of Japan made by the Portuguese before the closure of Japan. Tokyo, Tōyō Bunko [1966-67] 3 v. maps. (Tōyō Bunko ronsō, dai 48)

GA1243.5.A1N3 Orien Japan

Bibliographical footnotes.

In Japanese. Volume 2 has an English summary, and volume 3 is an atlas with maps that show the evolution of Japanese cartography.

236
Needham, Joseph. Geography and cartography [of China]. *In his* Science and civilisation in China. v. 3. Cambridge [Eng.], University Press, 1959. p. 497-590. illus., maps.   DS721.N39 v. 3

A comprehensive survey of the history of geography and cartography of China from the earliest times to the 18th century. Emphasis is on the contributions of traditional Chinese civilization to mathematics and to the sciences of heaven and earth.

237
Neuenstein, *Ger. Hohenlohe-Zentralarchiv.* Inventar der handschriftlichen Karten im Hohenlohe-Zentralarchiv Neuenstein, bearb. von Karl Schumm. Karlsruhe, G. Braun, 1961. 212 p. maps. (Inventare der nichtstaatlichen Archive in Baden-Württemberg, Heft 8)   Z6028.N49

There are 1,046 titles, with author and place indexes, and an introduction by Mr. Schumm.

238
New York *(State). Secretary of state.* Catalogue of maps and surveys, in the offices of the secretary of state, state engineer and surveyor, and comptroller, and the New York state library. Printed by order of the Assembly and under the direction of the secretary of state, 1851, and revised, corrected and enlarged by order of the Assembly and under the direction of the secretary of state, by David E. E. Mix, C. E. Albany, C. Van Benthuysen, 1859. 375 p.   Z6027.N5N6

Maps are listed in chronological order under the repository. There is an alphabetical index.

239
New York *(State). State engineer and surveyor.* Catalogue of maps and papers in the Land bureau of the Department of the state engineer and surveyor, New York state. 1910. Comp. by Merritt Peckham, Jr. . . . Albany, J. B. Lyon company, state printers, 1911. p. 229-275, 731-742.   Z6027.N5N7

Reprinted from the Annual Report of the State Engineer and Surveyor for the fiscal year that ended Sept. 30, 1910.

More than 1,100 maps are listed, as well as a number of atlases and miscellaneous books.

240
Newberry Library, *Chicago. Edward E. Ayer collection.* List of manuscript maps in the Edward E. Ayer collection, comp. by Clara A. Smith. Chicago, 1927. 101 p.   Z6621.C53M

"Supplementary to this manuscript material the Ayer Collection contains many printed facsimiles of old manuscript charts and maps. . . . The Ayer Collection [also] contains a small but very good working collection of printed atlases up to the year 1800." See also item 316.

241
Nørlund, Niels Erik. Danmarks kortlaegning, en historisk fremstilling; udg. med støtte af Carlsbergfondet. 2. udg. Tiden til afslutningen af Videnskabernes selskabs opmaaling. København, Munskgaard, 1943- 77 p. illus., maps. (Geodaetisk Instituts publikationer, 4)   GA961.N62

Treats of historical maps specifically of Denmark, but actually of all Scandinavia. Contains an excellent summary and many fine facsimile reproductions of maps from Ptolemy to 1813.

242
Nordenskiöld, Nils Adolf Erik, *friherre.* Facsimile-atlas to the early history of cartography with reproductions of the most important maps printed in the XV and XVI centuries. Translated from the Swedish original by Johan Adolf Ekelöf and Clements R. Markham. Stockholm, 1889. Reprinted 1961 by Kraus Reprint Corp., New York. 141 p., 170 maps.   G1025.N72 1961 G&M

A comprehensive history of cartography from Ptolemy through the 16th century, as reflected in printed maps. It contains 51 large and 84 small reproductions of Ptolemaic, pseudo-Ptolemaic, and non-Ptolemaic maps. Each section includes annotated lists of printed maps, chronologically arranged.

243
– – – Periplus; an essay on the early history of charts and sailing-directions; translated from the Swedish original by Francis A. Bather. Stockholm, Norstedt, 1897. 208 p. illus., maps. (Burt Franklin Research and source works series, no. 52)   G1025.N73 1897a G&M

Reprint of the 1897 work published in Stockholm by P. A. Norstedt & Söner.   G1025.N73 1897 G&M

A key reference work devoted to manuscript maps from ancient times to about 1650. A companion volume to the author's *Facsimile-atlas,* it deals with medieval mappae mundi and portolan charts, as well as maps of northern Europe, Africa, Asia, America, and the Pacific. Under each heading the maps are described in chronological order, with numerous footnotes, references, annotations, and a comprehensive index. It contains some 60 facsimile reproductions of the more important maps, many of which had never before been reproduced.

244

North Carolina. *State Dept. of Archives and History.* The Eric Norden collection; an inventory of a group of survey plats drawn for the most part by the late Eric Norden and covering land areas located chiefly in southeastern North Carolina, compiled by Henry Howard Eddy and Frances Harmon. Raleigh, 1949. 40 p.   Z6027.N7N6

The maps are listed by counties. Includes a biographical sketch of Mr. Norden, who was born in 1869 and died in 1946. The collection was presented to the North Carolina Department of Archives and History in 1947 by Mrs. Eric Norden.

245

Oehme, Ruthhardt. Die Geschichte der Kartographie des deutschen Südwestens. Hrsg. von der Kommission für Geschichtliche Landeskunde in Baden-Wurttemberg. Konstanz, J. Thorbecke [c1961] 168 p. maps. (Arbeiten zum Historischen Atlas von Südwestdeutschland, Bd. 3)

GA871.O3

Bibliography: p. 146-150.

Traces the evolution of maps of southwestern Germany from the 13th through the 18th centuries.

246

Ortroy, Fernand Gratien van. Bibliographie de l'oeuvre de Pierre Apian. (Extrait du Bibliographe moderne, mars-octobre 1901.) Besançon, P. Jacquin, 1902. 120 p.   Z8040.O78

Reprinted in 1963 by Meridian, Amsterdam.   Z8040.O78 1963

A bibliography of the works of Pierre Apian (Apianus), with an introduction which includes biographical data.

247

— — — Bibliographie sommaire de l'oeuvre mercatorienne. Paris, Champion, 1918-20. 80 p.   Z8568.O78

"Extrait de la Revue des bibliothèques": 1914, p. [113]-148; 1915/16, p. [9]-30, [119]-141.

A bibliography of works by the several members of the Mercator family. Also includes a list of portraits of Gerard Mercator.

248

— — — Bio-bibliographie de Gemma Frisius, fondateur de l'école belge de géographie, de son fils Corneille et de ses neveux les Arsenius. Amsterdam, Meridian Pub. Co., 1966. 434 p. illus. A reprint of the edition published in Brussells in 1920.   G69.G3O7 1966

Biographical and bibliographical data relating to Gemma Frisius, to his son Corneille, and to Gauthier, Reme, Ambroise, Ferdinand, and Regnier Arsenius.

249

– – – L'oeuvre cartographique de Gérard et de Corneille de Jode. Amsterdam, Meridian Pub. Co., 1963. 130 p.   GA913.5.J6O7 1963

Originally published in 1914.

A catalog of the cartographic works of Gérard and Cornelis de Jode. Includes reproductions of title pages of several de Jode atlases.

250

Osley, Arthur S. Mercator: a monograph on the lettering of maps, etc. in the 16th century Netherlands with a facsimile and translation of his treatise on the italic hand and a translation of Ghim's Vita Mercatoris; with a foreword by R. A. Skelton. London, Faber, 1969. 209 p. illus., maps.   Z43.A3M6

Bibliography: p. 195-202.

"Dr. Osley's investigation into the processes by which Mercator learnt the italic hand and by which he extended its use . . . are presented with exact scholarship, with humour, and with urbanity. We may well think that no previous writer has more perceptively delineated the gentle, gifted, and universal scholar that Mercator was in his physical and intellectual environment. For good measure, Dr. Osley has thrown in the first complete translation of Walter Ghim's biography of Mercator, published in the year after his death."–Skelton.

251

Ostrowski, Wiktor. The ancient names and early cartography of Byelorussia: material for historical research and study. Rev. ed. London, W. Ostrowski, 1970. 20 p., 35 pl. illus., maps.   DK507.5.O8 1970

Includes some information on the general cartographical history of Russia, as well as of Byelorussia. There are a number of black-and-white reproductions of early maps.

252

Oxford. University. *Bodleian Library*. The large scale county maps of the British Isles, 1596-1850, a union list. Compiled in the Map Section of the Bodleian Library by Elizabeth M. Rodger. Oxford, 1960. 52 p.

Z6027.G7O9

"The large scale maps of the British Isles provide . . . an unrivalled source of material for the years 1700-1850, during which so many changes took place in the countryside." In this list, "titles are not included, merely the area covered by the map, if it is not the county of the heading." More than 800 maps are listed. There are also an introduction, a list of references, and an index.

253

Palmerlée, Albert E. Maps of Costa Rica; an annotated cartobibliography. Lawrence, University of Kansas Libraries, 1965. 358 p. (University of Kansas publications. Library series, no. 19)   Z6027.C83P33

Lists maps in libraries of Kansas University and the American Geographical Society, and in the Library of Congress. "Maps found in books and other publications have been included in addition to those published separately.... Individual entries are designed to give enough information so that a preliminary selection of necessary maps can be made from the list itself." Some 1,623 maps are described, and there is an alphabetical index.

254

Paris. Bibliothèque nationale. *Département des cartes et plans.* Catalogue des cartes nautiques sur vélin conservées au Département des cartes et plans. Par Myriem Foncin, Marcel Destombes, et Monique de La Roncière. Paris, Bibliothèque nationale, 1963. 317 p.   Z6028.P3

Bibliography: p. [225]-258.

Descriptions of more than 180 vellum manuscript portolan charts. Annexes include indexes, a comprehensive bibliography relating to the literature of portolan charts, and lists of catalogs of portolan chart exhibits and of dealers' catalogs.

255

Pattison, William D. Beginnings of the American rectangular survey system, 1784-1800. Chicago, University of Chicago, 1957. 248 p. (Dept. of Geography. Research paper no. 50)   H31.C514, no. 50

Thesis—University of Chicago.

"The present study was prepared in order to increase our understanding of the American rectangular land system. Divided into three parts, the study consists of a report on the early years of the system's existence." There is an extensive bibliography.

256

Pennsylvania. *Division of Archives and Manuscripts.* Inventory of Canal Commissioners' maps in the Pennsylvania State Archives. Compiled by Martha L. Simonetti. Harrisburg, Bureau of Archives and History, Pennsylvania Historical and Museum Commission, 1968. 91 p.   Z6027.P4A5

Keyed to the descriptive index, Pennsylvania Board of Canal Commissioners' records (Harrisburg, 1959).

"This detailed listing ... is intended as a key to one of the most interesting and attractive groupings of cartographic and illustrative materials in the State Archives." Maps cover the period 1810-81.

257
Penrose, Boies. Travel and discovery in the Renaissance, 1420-1620. Cambridge, Harvard University Press, 1955. 376 p. illus., maps.   G95.P45 1955

Chapter 16 (p. 241-273) deals with "the cartography and navigation of the Renaissance." There is a 20-page bibliography.

258
Peru. *Ministerio de Relaciones Exteriores. Departamento de Archivo y Biblioteca.* Catálogo de la mapoteca; del siglo XVI al siglo XX. Lima, 1957.
Z6028.P4

Contents.—t. 1. Mapas. 512 p.

This list, which includes principally maps of South America and Peru, was compiled by Carlos Ortiz de Zevallos Paz-Soldan, Director, Departamento de Archivo y Biblioteca. Titles are arranged alphabetically by author within century groups, and there is an alphabetical index.

259
Peutinger Table. Die Peutingersche Tafel. Neudruck der letzten von Konrad Miller bearb. Aufl. einschliesslich seiner Neuzeichnung des verlorenen 1. Segments mit farbiger Wiedergabe der Tafel, sowie kurzer Erklärung und 18 Kartenskizzen der überlieferten römischen Reisewege aller Länder. Stuttgart, F. A. Brockhaus Komm.-Gesch., Abt. Antiquarium, 1962. 16 p. maps.
G1026.P4M5 1962 G&M

Folded colored map (facsimile on sheet 23 x 369 cm.) has title: Tabula quae dicitur Peutingeriana.

A reprinting of the work which was originally published in 1887-88 by Otto Maier, Ravensburg.

Miller provides an introductory analytical description of the Peutinger Table, one of the few surviving examples of Roman cartography, and a colored, reduced-scale reproduction of the map.

260
Phillips, Philip Lee. A descriptive list of maps and views of Philadelphia in the Library of Congress, 1683-1865. Philadelphia, Geographical Society of Philadelphia, 1926. 91 p.   Z6027.P54P5

"This list is confined entirely to material in the Library of Congress. . . . Attention is especially called to the rich collection of Revolutionary War material." The list includes 490 maps.

261
— — — . . . Guiana and Venezuela cartography. Washington, Govt. Print. Off., 1898. 53 p. (*In* American Historical Association. Annual Report . . . for 1897; Washington, 1898. p. 681-776).   Z6027.G94P5
Z6027.V45P5

"Considerable use was made of this list by the Venezuelan Boundary Commission, and much of it was furnished by me for publication in volume three of this report of this Commission. Enough, however, remains with recent additions to induce me to publish it in separate form."

262
– – – A list of books, magazine articles, and maps relating to Brazil 1800-1900 . . . A supplement to the Handbook of Brazil (1901) compiled by the Bureau of the American Republics. Washington, Govt. Print. Off., 1901. 145 p.   Z1671.P56

The maps (p. 107-145) are listed chronologically. See also item 164.

263
– – – A list of books, magazine articles, and maps relating to Chile. Comp. for the International Bureau of the American Republics. Washington, Govt. Print. Off., 1903. 110 p.   Z1716.P45

The publication is "intended as a guide to those who may desire to extend their researches further than the works bearing on this part of America which are usually found mentioned in catalogues already published." The maps (p. 74-110) are listed chronologically.

264
– – – Virginia cartography; a bibliographical description. Washington, Smithsonian Institution, 1896. 85 p. (Smithsonian miscellaneous collection [vol. XXXVII, art. IV]). Publication 1039.   Z6027.V81P5

Maps dating from 1585 to 1893 are described in varying detail. To inform scholars and others of the importance of maps "especially in connection with Virginia—a portion of America which in early days embraced much of that which is now known as the United States—is the object of [this] monograph."

265
Pigafetta, Antonio. First voyage around the world, by Antonio Pigafetta, and De Moluccis Insulis, by Maximilianus Transylvanus. With an introd. by Carlos Quirino. Manila, Filipiniana Book Guild, 1969. 162 p. illus. (Publications of the Filipiniana Book Guild, 14)   G420.M2P6113 1969b
Includes bibliographical references.

The first work is a translation, by James A. Robertson, of Pigafetta's account of Magellan's voyage around the world. The second work is the English version of a letter from Maximilianus Transylvanus to the Most Reverend Cardinal of Salzburg, which Henry Stevens translated and published in *Johann Schöner* (London, 1888).

266

– – – Magellan's voyage; a narrative account of the first circumnavigation. Introduction and translation by R. A. Skelton of the French manuscript entitled "Navigation et descouurement de la Inde superieure et isles de Malucque ou naissent les cloux de girofle" in the Beinecke Rare Book and Manuscript Library of Yale University Press, 1969. 2 v. illus., maps.

G420.M2P6113

Volume 2 is a colored facsimile of the original manuscript, including maps. "The manuscript here reproduced and translated is one of the most important geographical manuscripts known, and one of the handsomest."

267

– – – The voyage of Magellan, the journal of Antonio Pigafetta. A translation by Paula Spurlin Paige from the edition in the William L. Clements Library, University of Michigan, Ann Arbor. Englewood Cliffs, N.J., Prentice-Hall, 1969. 152 [201] p. maps.   G286.M2P543

The text of the original Paris edition (1525) of Pigafetta's journal is reproduced, with English translation on facing pages. There are facsimiles of five of the maps which accompany the journal. There are an introduction by Howard H. Peckham and a prefatory note to the translation by Paula Spurlin Paige.

268

Portugal. *Arquivo Histórico Ultramarino.* Catálogo da exposição cartográfica e iconográfica comemorativa do v centenário da morte do infante D. Henrique. Lisboa, 1960. 112 p. illus., maps.   Z6028.P83

Catalog of an exhibit arranged in commemoration of the fifth centenary of the death of Prince Henry the Navigator. There are 305 annotated titles; general area, geographical, and chronological indexes; and a number of reproductions, several in color.

269

Preuss, Charles. Exploring with Frémont; the private diaries of Charles Preuss. Translated and edited by Erwin G. and Elizabeth K. Gudde. Norman, University of Oklahoma Press [1958] 162 p. illus., maps.   F592.P713

Preuss was cartographer on John C. Frémont's first, second, and fourth expeditions to the Far West. "His claim to a niche in western American history rests upon his cartographical achievements. His maps were the first of the territory between the Mississippi and the Pacific Ocean based on modern principles of geodesy and cartography."

270

Quirino, Carlos. Philippine cartography, 1320-1899. 2d rev. ed. With an introduction by R. A. Skelton. Amsterdam, N. Israel [1963] 140 p. illus., maps.

GA1231.Q5 1963

"A book . . . on Philippine cartography has become not only timely but a necessity insofar as students of local history are concerned. By poring over innumerable maps, books and atlases, the author has been able to gather fragments of present-day knowledge in order to present a composite picture that is as accurate and historically comprehensive as is humanly possible."— Introduction. There is a chronological list of the charts of the Philippines.

271
Radford, Philip J. Antique maps. Denmark, Portsmouth (Hants.) P. J. Radford, 1965. 46 p. illus., maps.   GA231.R3

Bibliography: p. 44.

Reduced-scale reproductions of some 34 old maps, each with a short descriptive essay. "My object in writing this little book is not to attempt a reference book or learned work on cartography . . . but to supply a brief introduction to the subject."

272
Raistrick, Arthur. Yorkshire maps and map-makers. Clapham, via Lancaster, Dalesman, 1969. 72 p. illus., maps.   GA795.Y6R3

A brief general history of British, as well as Yorkshire, cartography.

273
Ravenstein, Ernest George, *and Sir* Charles Frederick Arden-Close. History of cartography. *In* Encyclopaedia Britannica. 14th ed., v. 14. London, New York, 1929. p. 836-845.   AE5.E363 1929, v. 14

A readily available, concise history, touching on the important steps in cartographic development.

274
Remezov, Semen U. The atlas of Siberia. Facsim. ed. with an introd. by Leo Bagrow. 's-Gravenhage, Mouton, 1958. 17 p., facsim.: 171 l. (Imago Mundi; a review of early cartography. Supplement 1)   G2160.R39 1958 G&M

Remezov's atlas was begun in 1697 and completed in 1701. A biographical sketch of Remezov, by Bagrow, was published in *Imago Mundi* (v. 11 (1954), p. 111-125). The atlas was never published and the manuscript edition, known under the name Khorograficheskaya Chertezhnaya Kniga, from which the facsimile was made, is now in the Harvard University Library.

275
Reps, John William. The making of urban America; a history of city planning in the United States. Princeton, N.J., Princeton University Press, 1965. 574 p. illus., maps.   NA9105.R45

Bibliography: 545-562.

"This book is an attempt to describe and assess the planning of [American] towns and cities founded from the time of colonial settlement to the beginning of the present era." There are more than 300 reproductions of early maps and views.

276

− − − Monumental Washington; the planning and development of the Capital center. Princeton, N.J., Princeton University Press, 1967. 221 p. illus., maps.
NA9127.W2R4

Bibliography: p. 206-211.

"The chief theme of this study is the plan prepared for the central portion of Washington in 1901 and the fate of its proposals." There are reproductions of a number of plans and maps of the city at various dates.

277

Rey Pastor, Julio, *and* Ernesto García Camarero. La cartografía mallorquina. Madrid, Departamento de Historia y Filosofía de la Ciencia, "Instituto Luis Vivas," Consejo Superior de Investigaciones Científicas, 1960. 207 p.
GA1005.M3R4

Bibliography: p. [171]-191.

About the Mallorcan cartographers who produced portolan charts during the 14th, 15th, and 16th centuries. There are brief biographical sketches of a number of the cartographers.

278

Richeson, Allie Wilson. English land measuring to 1800; instruments and practices. Cambridge, Mass., Published jointly by Society for the History of Technology, and M.I.T. Press [1966] 214 p. illus., map. (Society for the History of Technology. Monograph series, no. 2)   TA526.G72R5

Bibliography: p. 189-207.

"This history of surveying presents the development of land measuring in England from its origin in pre-Roman times through 1800. Although emphasis is upon the development of the science of surveying and the construction of the necessary instruments for its conduct, human activities closely related to surveying are also discussed." A selected bibliography is appended.

279

Richter, Herman. Olaus Magnus Carta marina 1539. Lund; [Stockholm Almqvist & Wiksell (distr.)] 1967. 194 p. [32] facsimiles. (Lynchnos-bibliotek, 11:2)   GA954 1539.M3R5

Bibliography: p. 170-183.

Includes biographical and historical information about Olaus Magnus and his cartographical work. There are facsimile reproductions of text, illustrations, and maps.

280
Ristow, Walter W., comp. A la carte; selected papers on maps and atlases. Washington, Library of Congress, 1972. 232 p. illus.   GA231.R5

Includes bibliographical references.

Reprints 20 papers, by various authors, which describe a number of historical maps and atlases. All but two of the papers were originally published in the *Quarterly Journal of the Library of Congress.*

281
— — — Facsimiles of rare historical maps; a list of reproductions for sale by various publishers and distributors. Compiled by Walter W. Ristow, assisted by Mary E. Graziani. 3d ed., rev. and enl. Washington, Geography and Map Division, Library of Congress, 1968. 20 p.   Z6022.U5 1968

Data presented have been compiled from information supplied by publishers or distributors. Reprinted, with supplement, in 1970.

282
Ritchie, George S. The Admiralty chart; British naval hydrography in the nineteenth century. New York, Amer. Elsevier Pub. Co., 1967. 388 p. illus., maps.   VK597.G72R5 1967a

Also published in London by Hollis & Carter, 1967.   VK597.G72R5

Bibliography: p. [373]-379.

This "story tells how the Admiralty belatedly appointed a civilian Hydrographer in 1795, and after reviewing the Englishmen engaged in chart-making at the time and describing the instruments available to them, goes on to show how the continuing absence of good printed charts in the midst of the Napoleonic Wars led to a more vigorous policy for providing the Fleet."

283
Robinson, Adrian H. W. Marine cartography in Britain: a history of the sea chart to 1855. With a foreword by John Edgell. [Leicester] Leicester University Press, 1962. 222 p. illus., maps.   GA791.R6

A good summary history of British nautical cartography. Also includes a bibliography, biographical notes of chartmakers, and list of charts.

284
Robinson, William W. Maps of Los Angeles from Ord's survey of 1849 to the end of the boom of the eighties. Los Angeles, Dawson's Bookshop, 1966. 87 p.   GA413.R6

"Selective list of maps of Los Angeles": p. 37-87.

A limited edition of 380 copies printed by Saul & Lillian Marks at the Plantin Press, Los Angeles, Calif., 1966. "My approach to the historical maps of the Los Angeles area has not been through published material. Hence, I present no bibliography. Rather, the approach has been to the sources of maps: the collections, private, public, or institutional, where maps abound. ... The phrase 'Los Angeles area', as used ... throughout the book, has reference to all of present-day Los Angeles and Orange counties." Of the 127 items described, 27 are illustrated by map reproductions in color.

285
Rohr, Heinz. Die Entwicklung des Kartenbildes Westeuropas zwischen Kanal und Mittelmeer von den ältesten Weltkarten bis Mercator. Borna-Leipzig, Spezialbetrieb für Dissertationsdruck von R. Noske, 1939. 283 p.

GA781.R6

"Literatur": p. 279-283.

Summarizes cartography of western Europe to about 1569. There are sections on scriptural maps, portolan charts, and 15th- and 16th-century world maps. Seventy titles are listed in the references.

286
Royal Institution of Chartered Surveyors. Five centuries of maps & map-making. An exhibition at 12 Great George Street, Westminster [10th June-4th July 1953. London] 127 p.   GA190.L65R6

"Main object [in the exhibit] has been to illustrate the development of surveying and map-making as a science in [Great Britain] from the 16th century. Probably no previous exhibition of British maps and map-making has been so complete." In all, 999 maps, ranging in date from 1504 to 1945, are described.

287
Ruge, Sophus. Die Entwicklung der Kartographie von Amerika bis 1570. Hildesheim, G. Olms, 1962. 85 p. maps.   GA401.R92 1962

A reprint edition of a classic work on the early cartography of America, originally published in 1892.

288
Salishchev, Konstantin Alekseevich. Osnovy kartovedeniĩa: istoriĩa kartografii i kartograficheskie istochniki (Principles of cartography: historical cartography and cartographical materials). 3d rev. ed. Moscow, Geodezizdat, 1959-62. 2 v. illus., maps.   GA105.S253

A general treatise on cartography, in Russian. Volume 2 includes a section on the history of cartography.

289
Sandler, Christian. Johann Baptista Homann, Matthäus Seutter und ihre Landkarten; ein Beitrag zur Geschichte der Kartographie. Amsterdam, Meridian Pub. Co. [196-?] 97 p. map.   GA873.6.H6S2

Biographical information on Johann Baptista Homann and Matthäus Seutter, and cartobibliographical data about their map and atlas publications. With bibliographic references.

290

Santarem, Manuel Francisco de Barros. 2. *visconde* de. Essai sur l'histoire de la cosmographie et de la cartographie pendant le moyen-âge et sur les progres de la geographie après les grandes découvertes du XVe siècle, pour servir d'introduction et d'explication à l'Atlas composé de mappemondes et de portulans . . . depuis le VIe siècle de notre ere jusqu'au XVIIe. Paris, Impr. Maulde et Renou, 1849-52. 3 v. and portfolio of 79 maps.

G89.S2 text
G1025.S3 1849 atlas

Volume 1 contains a general summary of the development of cartography and geographic theories during the early Middle Ages. Though largely out of date in details, this great work remains one of the primary approaches to medieval geography.

291

Sanz López, Carlos. Bibliotheca Americana vetustissima; últimas adiciones. Madrid, Librería General Victoriano Suárez, 1960. 2 v. (1,407 p.)

Z1202.H3152

– – – Bibliotheca Americana vetustissima; comentario crítico e índice general cronológico de los seis volúmenes que componen la obra. Madrid, Librería General Victoriano Suárez, 1960. 79 p.   Z1202.H315

The first describes cartographical and historical works not included in Henry Harrisse's publication with the same title (item 144). There are a number of small-scale reproductions of early maps. The commentary and index pertain to Harrisse's original work as well as to this supplement.

292

– – – Cartografia histórica de los descubrimientos australes. Madrid, Impr. Aguirre, 1967. 96 p. maps. (Publicaciones de la Real Sociedad Geográfica. Serie B, no. 471)   GA1681.S25

Bibliographical footnotes.

Traces the origin and evolution of the earliest appearance of the legendary "Terra Australis Incognita" on maps. There are reduced-scale reproductions of a number of maps.

293

– – – La Geographia de Ptolomeo, ampliada con los primeros mapas impresos de América, desde 1507; estudio bibliográfico y crítico, con el catálogo de las ediciones aparecidas desde 1475 a 1883, comentado e ilustrado. Madrid, Librería General V. Suárez, 1959. 281 p. illus., maps.   Z8715.S35

About Ptolemy's *Geography* and its several editions, including a chapter on "works erroneously considered as Ptolemy editions." There is a synoptic table of all editions of the *Geography,* and the volume includes reproductions of plates from a number of Ptolemy editions.

294
– – – Mapas antiguos del mundo (siglos XV-XVI). Reproducidos y comentados por Carlos Sanz. [Madrid, 1962] 157 p. and atlas (50 maps).
G1025.S35 1962 G&M

At head of title: Bibliotheca Americana vetustissima.
"Obras completas de Carlos Sanz": p. [151]-157.

– – – – – – Suplemento. Descritos y comentados por Carlos Sanz. [Madrid, 1968] 29 p. and atlas (9 maps). G1025.S35 1962 Suppl. G&M

The atlas volume contains reduced-scale reproductions of 50 maps that trace the discovery and cartographic evolution of America. The second volume includes brief descriptive comments on each of the maps.

295
– – – El nombre América; libros y mapas que lo impusieron; descripción y crítica histórica. Madrid, Suárez, 1959. 244 p. illus., maps. E125.V6S26

A discussion of the use of the name "America" and of the earliest maps on which it appears.

296
Schaaf, William Leonard. Carl Friedrich Gauss, prince of mathematicians. New York, Watts, [1964] 168 p. illus., maps. QA29.G3S3

Bibliography: p. 162.

Gauss, who was born in Brunswick, Germany, Apr. 30, 1777, made contributions in the field of cartography and geodesy as well as in mathematics.

297
Scotland. National Library, *Edinburgh.* Shelf-catalogue of the Wordie collection of polar exploration. Boston, G. K. Hall, 1964. 191 p. Z6005.P7S18

The catalog is photographically reproduced from the original typed and manuscript record. "It is important to remember that this catalogue was prepared primarily for staff use and is essentially a check list." The catalog includes some maps as well as cartographical references.

298
Scotland. *Record Office.* Descriptive list of plans. By Ian H. Adams. Edinburgh, H.M.S.O., 1966-70. 2 v. GA812.A5

"Most of the plans in the Register House series were executed in the century from about 1750 to 1850. Many are manuscript; others are engraved or lithographed. . . ." Volume 1 covers RHP. 1 to RHP. 1200, representing accessions between 1849 and 1961. Basic arrangement is by counties, in alphabetical order. Introduction includes information on the cartographic history of Scotland. Volume 2 includes accessions to the collection between 1961 and 1963.

299
Sharaf, 'Abd al-'Aziz Turayh. A short history of geographical discovery. Alexandria, M. Zaki el Mahdy [1963] 417 p. illus., maps.   G80.S5
    Bibliography: p. 378-395.

"The general aim of this book is to present an outline of the development of geographical discovery, both in practice and theory, from the earliest recorded times to the contemporary period." Special emphasis is laid on Muslim achievements in the field of geographical discovery and the exploration of Africa. There is a comprehensive bibliography.

300
Sinnatamby, J. R. Ceylon in Ptolemy's Geography. [Colombo, 1968] 73 p. maps.   DS489.S54

"This work deals with some aspects of Ptolemy's *Geography* in general and with the identification of some names on Ptolemy's map of Ceylon."

301
Skelton, Raleigh A. Captain James Cook—after two hundred years: a commemorative address delivered before the Hakluyt Society. London, British Museum, 1969. 32 p. 25 plates, illus., maps.   G246.C7S55
    Bibliography: p. 31-32.

"Cook as a man, and as a man of the eighteenth century, is a proper subject for study." Among the illustrations are reproductions of maps drawn by Cook.

302
– – – County atlases of the British Isles, 1579-1850; a bibliography. London, Map Collectors' Circle, 1964-70. 5 parts. (Map collectors' series, nos. 9, 14, 41, 49, 63)   Z6003.M3 no. 9, 14, 41, 49, 63
    Issued in parts.
    Supersedes Thomas Chubb's The printed maps in the atlases of Great Britain and Ireland; a bibliography, 1579-1870.
    Contents:–No. 9. Part 1, 1579-1612.–No. 14. Part 2, 1612-46.–No. 41. Part 3, 1627-70.–No. 49. Part 4, 1671-1703.–No. 63. Part 5, 1579-1703: appendixes.

    Also published by Carta Press, London, 1970- facsims., maps, ports.
                                                                          Z6027.G7S55

A comprehensive catalog of county atlases of the British Isles. "The bibliography . . . is not to be considered a mere revision of Chubb [see item 70] ; it has been rewritten throughout and is entirely new both in substance and in form. The text of the descriptive notices, on a more systematic plan, is new, and it includes bibliographical descriptions, besides a general discussion of each new atlas and its history." Dr. Skelton died in 1970, before the study was completed.

303

– – – Decorative printed maps of the 15th to 18th centuries; a rev. ed. of Old decorative maps and charts, by A. L. Humphreys. With eighty-four reproductions and a new text by R. A. Skelton. London, Spring Books [1966, c1952] 80 p. illus., maps.   G1025.S6 1966 G&M

Includes bibliographies.

Revision of the 1952 edition, published in London and New York, by Staples Press.   G1025.S6 1952

A concise introduction to cartographical development useful to the collector and student alike. It contains numerous reproductions of pertinent maps and has a general bibliography and references at the end of each chapter.

304

– – – Explorers' maps; chapters in the cartographic record of geographical discovery. [New ed.] Feltham, N.Y., Spring Books, 1970. 337 p. illus., maps.
GA203.S55 1970

Bibliography: p. 328.

Revision of the 1958 edition, published by Praeger in New York City (GA203.S55), and by Routledge & Paul, in London (GA203.S55 1958a).

"The book may be regarded as a pictorial comparison to general histories of exploration. . . . The maps used or drawn by explorers describe the borderland between the known and the unknown. . . . The text is planned as a concise summary of geographical ideas and events associated with the maps reproduced." Includes reproductions of many early maps.

305

– – – Looking at an early map. Lawrence, University of Kansas Libraries, 1965. 29 p. 9 plates. (University of Kansas Publications. Library series, 17)
GA231.S5

The annual public lecture on books and bibliography given at the University of Kansas, October 1962.

The paper discusses "the critical controls which must govern our study of early maps and our inferences from them. . . . The early map under our eyes is the end product of a complex series of processes—assembly of information from various sources and in different forms, both graphic and textual; assimilation to the mapmaker's geographical ideas, to transmitted cartographic patterns, or his political interest; and the resultant stages of compilation, control, adjustment, and copying. Only after study of this background can we look over the mapmaker's shoulder and begin to perceive why he drew this outline or made that identification or associated certain place names with a particular feature." There is a list of some 40 *Notes*.

306

– – – Maps, a historical survey of their study and collecting. Chicago, University of Chicago Press, 1972. 138 p.

"Published for the Hermon Dunlap Smith Center for the History of Cartography, the Newberry Library."
"The Kenneth Nebenzahl, Jr., Lectures in the History of Cartography at the Newberry Library."
Contents:–1. The history of cartography: an introductory survey.–2. The preservation and collection of early maps.–3. The historical study of early maps: past.–4. The historical study of early maps: present and future.

The lectures printed in this volume were originally delivered in 1966. Because of Dr. Skelton's death in 1970, the volume was edited for publication by David Woodward. In addition to the four lectures, there is a comprehensive bibliography of the published works of R. A. Skelton which was compiled by Robert A. Karrow, Jr.

307

– – – The Vinland map and the Tartar relation, by R. A. Skelton, Thomas E. Marston, and George D. Painter for the Yale University Library. With a foreword by Alexander O. Vietor. New Haven, Yale University Press, 1965. 291 p. illus., maps.   GA308.Z65S55

A comprehensive scholarly study of the higly publicized Vinland Map. "The Vinland Map contains the earliest known and indisputable cartographic representation of any part of the Americas."

308

Smith, Edgar Crosby, *ed.* Moses Greenleaf; Maine's first map-maker. A biography: with letters, unpublished manuscripts and a reprint of Mr. Greenleaf's rare paper on Indian place-names; also a bibliography of the maps of Maine. Bangor [Me.], Printed for the De Burians [by C. H. Glass & Co.] 1902. 183 p. illus., maps.   GA428.S64

"Bibliography of the Maps of Maine": p. [137]-165. This was also issued separately in 1903.

"The only biography of one of the most remarkable men which our state ever had." Greenleaf published a map of Maine, the first edition of which was issued in 1815. There are entries for 152 maps in the bibliography.

309

Smith, Thomas R., *and* Bradford L. Thomas. Maps of the 16th to 19th centuries in the University of Kansas Libraries; an analytical carto-bibliography.

Lawrence, University of Kansas Libraries, 1963. 137 p. (University of Kansas publications. Library series, no. 16)   Z6028.S55

Bibliography: p. 131-132.

Some 254 maps, dating from 1570 to mid-19th century, are described with annotations. Most are taken from atlases and are listed in a classed geographical area arrangement. There is an alphabetical index of proper names.

310

Society for the History of Discoveries. Terrae incognitae, the annals of the Society for the history of discoveries. Amsterdam, N. Israel. ann. 1969-Ed. Bruce B. Solnick.   G&M Div.

"Terrae Incognitae is viewed as an Annual that is both catholic and eclectic in its search for appropriate articles. . . . geographic exploration, the techniques, impact, and literature of discoveries, whenever and wherever they took place, will be our primary interest." Three volumes had been published through 1971.

311

Spain. *Archivo General de Indias, Seville.* Relación descriptiva de los mapas, planos, & de México y Floridas, existentes en el Archivo General de Indias, por Pedro Torres Lanzas. Seville, Imp. de Mercantil, 1900. 2 v. in 1.

Z6027.M6S6

A listing of 516 maps in a chronological arrangement, with an author index. Photoreproductions of a number of the early manuscript maps of America are in the collections of the Library of Congress Geography and Map Division.

312

Spain. *Ejército. Servicio Geográfico.* Catálogo de atlas. [Madrid] 1962. 420 p.

Z6028.S76

At head of title: Archivo de Planos.

Ranging in date from 1501 to the 20th century, the 329 atlases described are arranged chronologically, within century divisions. Entries include contents and annotations. There is an introduction by Col. Luis Aparacio Miranda.

313

Spekke, Arnolds. The Baltic Sea in ancient maps. [Translated from the Latvian by A. J. Grinbergs and others.] Stockholm, M. Goppers, 1961. 75 p. illus., maps.   GS951.S713

Bibliography: p. 75-[76].

"The object of the book is to present to the reader interested in ancient Baltic history an individual historic-cartographic picture of the Baltic Sea and its eastern shores in particular, up to the threshold of modern times." There are 14 reproductions of early maps.

314
Stahl, William H. Ptolemy's Geography; a select bibliography. New York, The New York Public Library, 1953. 86 p.   Z8715.S82

"Reprinted from the Bulletin of the New York Public Library of 1951-1952."

"It would be far too ambitious for one bibliographer to attempt to uncover a large proportion of all the studies and significant observations that have been made on Ptolemy.... The present bibliography is the meagerest introduction to such an undertaking." There are, nonetheless, 1,464 citations in a classified arrangement, with an author index.

315
Stauffer, David M. American engravers upon copper and steel. New York, The Grolier Club of the city of New York, 1907. 2 v.   NE505.S8

Contents:—pt. 1. Biographical sketches.—pt. 2. Checklist of the works of the earlier engravers.

A good index to early American engravers, many of whom engraved maps. See also item 105.

316
Stevens, Henry N. Ptolemy's Geography; a brief account of all the printed editions down to 1730, with notes on some important variations observed in that of Ulm 1482, including the recent discovery of the earliest printed map of the world yet known on modern geographical conceptions in which some attempt was made to depart from ancient traditions. 2d ed. London, H. Stevens, son and Stiles, 1908. 62 p. illus.   Z8715.S89

Reprinted in 1972 by Theatrum Orbis Terrarum, Amsterdam.

Based on the Henry Stevens Ptolemy Collection, which is now in the Edward E. Ayer Collection, Newberry Library, Chicago.

317
Stevenson, Edward Luther. Terrestrial and celestial globes; their history and construction, including a consideration of their value as aids in the study of geography and astronomy. New Haven, Pub. for the Hispanic Society of America by the Yale University Press, 1921. 2 v. illus. (Publications of the Hispanic Society of America, no. 86)   GA260.S7

"Bibliographical list": v. 2, p. 220-248.

A comprehensive work, including an extensive bibliography, an index of globemakers with locations of globes, and a general index.

318

Stokes, Isaac Newton Phelps. The iconography of Manhattan Island, 1498-1909. [Compiled from original sources and illustrated by photo-intaglio reproductions of important maps, plans, views and documents in public and private collections. New York] Arno Press [1967] 6 v. illus., maps.   F128.3.S856

Reprint of the 1915-28 edition published by R. H. Dodd, New York.
F128.37.S87

Bibliography by Victor H. Paltsists: v. 6, p. [181]-281.

Includes many reproductions of early maps and extensive notes about the early maps of New York City and their makers.

319

Stowell, Robert Frederick. A Thoreau gazetteer. Edited by William L. Howarth. Princeton, N.J., Princeton University Press, 1970. 56 p. illus., maps.   PS3052.S7 1970

Includes bibliographical references.

"This *Gazetteer* ... attempts to provide a geographical guide to the writings of Thoreau by including maps of three varieties: those drawn by Thoreau himself, those contemporary with his time, and those reconstructed from his accounts and other sources."—Introduction.

320

Stuart-Stubbs, Basil. Maps relating to Alexander MacKenzie: a keepsake distributed at a meeting of the Bibliographical Society of Canada, Jasper Park, June, 1968 [by] Stuart-Stubbs. n.p. 1968? [33] l. 12 maps. Z6027.C21S78

"This collection of maps was assembled to illustrate one method of describing old maps. It is not a complete list of all maps relating to Alexander MacKenzie, nor are the descriptions themselves complete in all cases. However, it could serve as the beginning of a cartobibliography of MacKenzie."

321

Swem, Earl Gregg, *comp.* Maps relating to Virginia in the Virginia State Library and other departments of the Commonwealth with the 17th and 18th century atlas-maps in the Library of Congress. Richmond, D. Bottom, Superintendent of public printing, 1914. 263 p. (*In* Virginia. State library. Bulletin. v. 7, no. 2/3, 1914)   Z6027.V81V6

"In general, the plan has been to catalog maps which relate to the territory in the present State of Virginia through April 1914, and those relating to West Virginia through 1863, including some of those which illustrate the different boundaries and claims in the Colonial period." The arrangement is chronological, and the list is supplemented by an alphabetical index.

322
Taylor, Eva Germaine Rimington. Late Tudor and early Stuart geography, 1583-1650; a sequel to Tudor geography, 1485-1583. New York, Octagon Books, 1968. 322 p. illus. G95.T29 1968

A reprint of the 1934 edition published by Methuen.

Bibliography: p. 177-298.

The "writer's purpose is not to reconstruct the geography of the seventeenth century as it was, but as men believed it to be." There is a bibliography with close to 2,000 entries.

323
– – – Tudor geography, 1485-1583. New York, Octagon Books, 1968. 290 p. illus., maps. G95.T3 1968

A reprint of the book originally published by Methuen in 1930.

Bibliography: p. 163-243.

This volume "deals only with that fateful century or so during which Englishmen of all ranks were forced gradually by circumstances to think geographically as they had never done before." There are many references to cartography, globes, and maps. There is an appended "Catalogue of English geographical or kindred works (printed books and MSS.) to 1583."

324
Teleki, Pál, gróf. Atlas zur Geschichte der Kartographie der Japanischen Inseln. Nebst dem holländischen Journal der Reise Mathys Quasts und A. J. Tasmans zur Entdeckung der Goldinseln im Osten von Japan i. d. J. 1639 und dessen deutscher Übersetzung. Authorized reprint. Nendeln, Liechtenstein, Kraus Reprint, 1966. 184 p. illus., maps. GA1241.T15 1966

Reprinted from the 1909 edition published in Leipzig by K. W. Hiersemann.

Bibliography: p. 179-184.

A major reference work on the history of Japanese cartography. The first part treats of early European knowledge of Japan from the travels of Marco Polo and its first appearance on the 1375 Catalan map up to 1550. The second part covers the period from the Portuguese discovery in 1542 to the end of the 18th century. Valuable indexes and an extensive bibliography are included.

325
Texas. State Library, Austin. The map collection of the Texas State archives 1527-1900. Compiled by James M. Day and Ann B. Dunlap. Austin, 1962. 156 p. Z6027.A5T4

"A reprint from the Southwestern historical quarterly, LXV, no. 3 (January, 1962); LXV, no. 4 (April, 1962); LXVI, no. 1 (July, 1962); LXVI, no. 2 (October, 1962)."

The maps are arranged chronologically and are identified by filing numbers as well as by titles. "The title used is that shown on the map. If the map has no specific title, one was created and brackets [ ] were used as a distinguishing feature." There is an alphabetical index.

326

Theatrum Orbis Terrarum; a series of atlases in facsimile. [Facsimile editions of old and rare atlases, pilot-books and seaman's guides] Advisory editors, R. A. Skelton and Alexander O. Vietor. Amsterdam, Theatrum Orbis Terrarum, 1963- G&M Div.

This facsimile series makes "available a corpus of early atlases and other works illustrating the progress of geographical and cartographical knowledge from the time of Ptolemy to the 17th century." Most volumes have introductory bibliographical notes by R. A. Skelton relating to the specific work and its producer.

327

Thomas, Bradford L. A biographical list of cartographers, engravers, and publishers of the XVI to XIX century maps in the University of Kansas Library. Lawrence, University of Kansas, Dept. of Geography, 1961. 21 l. illus.

GA198.T5

This "biographical list was compiled in the process of research conducted on the dates and origins of the sixteenth to nineteenth century maps in the collection of the University of Kansas Library." Some 250 brief biographies are included.

328

Thompson, Edmund B. Maps of Connecticut before the year 1800; a descriptive list. Windham, Conn., Hawthorn House, 1940. 66 p. maps.

Z6027.C75T5

This excellent compilation is a model for lists of maps of individual states. "The manuscripts make an interesting supplement to the list of printed maps and in some instances reveal sources that were available to early cartographers. [But] a greater emphasis in this study has been placed on the search for printed maps." Forty-four maps are described, in a chronological sequence. There is an author index.

329

– – – Maps of Connecticut for the years of industrial revolution, 1801-1860, a descriptive list. Windham, Conn., Hawthorn House, 1942. 111 p. maps.

Z6027.C75T52

This list continues Thompson's earlier compilation and includes descriptions of early 19th-century state maps and of the mid-century town and county maps which were produced largely by lithographic procedures. Approximately 140 maps are described. There is an introduction and an author list.

330
Thompson, Francis M. L. Chartered surveyors: the growth of a profession. London, Routledge & K. Paul, 1968. 400 p. illus., maps.   TA526.G7T52

Prepared to commemorate the centenary in 1968 of the Royal Institution of Chartered Surveyors. This "is neither a complete history of surveyors and surveying before the founding of the Institution nor a complete account and record of the activities of the institution during its first hundred years. It is an account of those features which seem most important, and of most interest in the formation and subsequent development of the profession."

331
Thomson, Don W. Men and meridians; the history of surveying and mapping in Canada. Ottawa, R. Duhamel, Queen's printer, 1966-69. 3 v. illus., maps.
                                                                TA523.A1T47
Contents:—v. 1. Prior to 1867.—v. 2. 1867 to 1917.—v. 3. 1917 to 1947.

A three-volume history of surveying and mapping in Canada that contains much excellent information on many aspects of the history of mapmaking.

332
Thrower, Norman J. W. Maps and man, an examination of cartography in relation to culture and civilization. Englewood Cliffs, N.J., Prentice-Hall, 1972. 184 p. illus.

"It is to provide information on the nature and development of maps and the lure and love of cartography that this book has been prepared."— Author's preface.

333
— — — Original survey and land subdivision; a comparative study of the form and effect of contrasting cadastral surveys. Chicago, Published for the Association of American Geographers by Rand McNally [1966] 160 p. illus., maps. (The Monograph series of the Association of American Geographers, 4)
                                                                TA522.O3T57

"The purpose of this study is to examine selected elements of the cultural landscape as developed, in areas that are of similar character but differ in the method used for the subdivision of land. . . . Two localities in the western half of Ohio have been studied in detail and are used to exemplify different survey systems."

334
— — — The terraqueous globe: the history of geography and cartography; papers read at a Clark Library seminar April 27, 1968, by Norman J. W. Thrower and Clarence J. Glacken. Los Angeles, William Andrews Clark Memorial Library. University of California, 1969. 80 p. maps.   G62.T48

Contents.—Edmond Halley and thematic geo-cartography, by N. J. W. Thrower.—On Chateaubriand's journey from Paris to Jerusalem, 1806-07, by C. J. Glacken.

The paper by Thrower calls attention to Halley's early use of thematic maps for showing climatic data. Thrower's paper "is not on Halley as a geophysicist or as a physical geographer, but is rather upon his contributions to thematic geo-cartography."

335
Tooley, Ronald Vere. Collectors' guide to maps of the African continent and southern Africa. London, Carta Press, 1969. 132 p. illus., maps.
Z6027.A2T65

Includes bibliographical references.

"The aim of this book is to provide an easy alphabetical guide to the collector of early printed maps of the whole continent of Africa, of Southern Africa and the Cape of Good Hope. It is not intended to list every known map of Africa . . . but to give a brief account of more than a hundred important mapmakers [and] describe and list many examples of their maps relating to Africa." There are reduced-scale reproductions of 100 maps.

336
— — — A dictionary of mapmakers, including cartographers, geographers, publishers, engravers, etc., from the earliest times to 1900. London, Map Collectors' Circle, 1965- [6] v. (Map collectors' series, no. 16, 28, 40, 50, 67, 78)
Z6003.M3, no. 16, 28, 40, 50, 67, 78

Issued in parts.

Brief listings, including birth and death dates and major works, of mapmakers of all countries. Additional parts are scheduled for future publication.

337
— — — Early maps of Australia, the Dutch period; being examples from the collection of R. V. Tooley, with bibliographical notes. London, Map Collectors' Circle, 1965. 27 p. maps. (Map collectors' series, no. 23)
Z6003.M3 no. 23

"The subject of this monograph is the second period [in the history of Australian cartography], that is the early Dutch discoveries prior to Tasman, Tasman's own voyages, of 1642-44, and the representation of Australia in maps up to 1770." There are 30 map reproductions.

338
— — — Maps and map-makers. 4th ed. London, Batsford, 1970. 140 p. illus., maps.
GA201.T6 1970

An introduction to the history of cartography designed for use by the collector as well as the student. It is concerned with atlases and maps published by the better known mapmakers from ancient times to the 19th century, arranged according to schools or nationalities. Lists of bibliographical references are found at the end of each chapter.

339
Traversi, Carlo. Storio della cartografia coloniale italiana. Roma, Instituto poligrafico dello Stato, 1964. 294 p. illus., maps. (Comitato per la documentazione dell'opera dell'Italia in Africa. L'Italia in Africa; serie scientifico-culturale)   GA1350.T7

Bibliography: p. 247-257.

A summary history of Italian cartographical achievements in the former Italian colonies in Africa. There are a number of map reproductions, an alphabetical index, and a comprehensive bibliography.

340
U.S. *Library of Congress.* List of books relating to Cuba (including references to collected works and periodicals) by A. P. C. Griffin . . . with a bibliography of maps, by P. Lee Phillips. Washington, U.S. Govt. Print. Off., 1898. 61 p. (U.S. 55th Cong., 2d sess., 1897-98. Senate. Doc. no. 161) Z1511.U54

The maps (p. 41-57) are listed chronologically.

341
U.S. *Library of Congress. Geography and Map Division.* Land ownership maps, a checklist of nineteenth century United States county maps in the Library of Congress. Compiled by Richard W. Stephenson. Washington, U.S. Govt. Print. Off., 1967. 86 p. illus., maps.   Z6027.U5U54

The checklist includes 1,449 items arranged alphabetically by counties and states. An introductory essay summarizes the history and development of U.S. county maps. Index.

342
U.S. *Library of Congress. Map Division.* Aviation cartography; a historico-bibliographic study of aeronautical charts, by Walter W. Ristow. 2d ed., rev. and enl. Washington, 1960, reprinted 1962. 245 p.   Z6026.A2U54 1960

There are 774 annotated references, an alphabetical index, and a 50-page introductory essay on the history and development of aeronautical charts.

343
– – – Civil War maps; an annotated list of maps and atlases in map collections of the Library of Congress, compiled by Richard W. Stephenson. Washington, 1961. 138 p.   Z6027.U5U55

Bibliography "describes those items in the collections of the Map Division which indicate troop positions and movements, engagements, and fortifications. The list also includes a number of commercially published 'theatre of war' maps which indicate in a very general way the location of forts and occasionally the places where battles occured." There are descriptions of 700 maps, with an alphabetical index.

344
– – – The Hotchkiss map collection; a list of manuscript maps, many of the Civil War period, prepared by Major Jed. Hotchkiss, and other manuscript and annotated maps in his possession, compiled by Clara Egli LeGear, with a foreword by Willard Webb. Washington, Library of Congress, 1951. 67 p.

Z6027.U5H6

There are descriptions of 341 maps and an alphabetical index.

345
– – – A list of geographical atlases in the Library of Congress, with bibliographical notes. Washington, U.S. Govt. Print. Off., 1909- 7 v.   Z6028.U56

Contents:–v. 1-4, compiled by Philip Lee Phillips.–v. 5-6, compiled by Clara Egli LeGear.–v. 7, compiled by C. E. LeGear, in press.

Reprint editions of volumes 1 to 4 have been published in Amsterdam by Theatrum Orbis Terrarum, Ltd.

Volumes 1-4 list 4,324 atlases dating from the Middle Ages through 1919. Volume 5 includes all world atlases acquired by the Library of Congress between 1920 and 1956. Full tables of contents are given for all published before 1820. Volume 6 lists atlases of Europe, Africa, and Asia acquired by the Library between 1920 and 1961. Volume 7 includes American atlases acquired between 1920 and 1968, as well as basic chronological lists of atlases, alphabetical author lists, and alphabetical indexes. For many of the older atlases there are extensive bibliographic notes and lists of individual maps (primarily "maps relating to America, plans of cities throughout the world, and material of specific interest not usually found in atlases").

346
– – – List of maps and views of Washington and District of Columbia in the Library of Congress, by P. Lee Phillips. Washington, U.S. Govt. Print. Off., 1900. 72 p. (56th Cong. 1st sess. Senate. Doc. 154)   Z6027.W32U5

The maps listed are arranged chronologically, dating from 1782 to 1900.

347
– – – A list of maps of America in the Library of Congress, preceded by a list of works relating to cartography. By P. Lee Phillips. Washington, Govt. Print. Off., 1901. 1,137 p.   Z6027.A5U5

Reprint editions published in 1967, by Burt Franklin in New York City (Z6027.A5U5 1967b) and by Theatrum Orbis Terrarum, Amsterdam (Z6027.A5U5 1967).

There are between 15,000 and 20,000 titles, arranged alphabetically by area, including separate maps as well as maps in atlases and in books. The *List* includes the maps of the Americas in the Library of Congress at the time the Division of Maps was established in 1897.

348

– – – Maps showing explorers' routes, trails & early roads in the United States; an annotated list compiled by Richard S. Ladd. Washington, U.S. Govt. Print. Off., 1962. 137 p. map.   Z6027.U5U56

Arrangement is alphabetical, by author. All of the 300 maps described are in the collections of the Library of Congress. There is an alphabetical index.

349

– – – Three-dimensional maps; an annotated list of references relating to the construction and use of terrain models. Compiled by Walter W. Ristow. 2d ed., rev. and enl. Washington, U.S. Govt. Print. Off., 1964 [i.e. 1965] 38 p.
Z6026.R4U6 1965

There are 395 annotated references and an introductory summary of the history and development of relief models.

350

– – – United States atlases; a list of national, state, county, city, and regional atlases in the Library of Congress, compiled by Clara Egli LeGear. Washington, U.S. Govt. Print. Off., 1950-53. 2 v. (445, 301 p.)   Z881.U5 1950at

The arrangement is by states, subdivided by counties, cities, regions, and date. More than 3,500 titles are listed. There is also an alphabetical author list. Volume 2 lists additons to the Library of Congress up to 1949 and holdings of 180 other libraries. A reprint edition of volume 1 was published by Arno Press in 1971.

351

U.S. *National Archives.* Civil War maps in the National Archives. Washington, U.S. Govt. Print. Off., 1964. 127 p. (*Its* Publication no. 64-12)
Z6027.U5U58

"The approximately 8,000 maps, charts, and plans described in this publication comprise the largest body of cartographic items pertaining to the American Civil War in existence. . . . Not included are maps that are filed with Civil War correspondence, reports, and similar documents." The arrangement is by the Archives' "Record Groups." There is an alphabetical index to proper names appearing in the guide.

352

– – – Geographical exploration and topographic mapping by the United States Government, 1777-1952; catalog. [Washington, 1952] 52 p. (*Its* Publication no. 53-2)   Z6027.U5U6

Describes documents in an exhibit at the National Archives, July 27 through September 1952.

353
– – – Guide to cartographic records in the National Archives [by Charlotte M. Ashby and others] Washington, for sale by the Supt. of Docs., U.S. Govt. Print. Off., 1971. 444 p. (*Its* Publications no. 71-16)   Z6028.U575

"This guide describes those [maps] that are maintained in the Cartographic Branch, but there are many maps filed with closely related documents in other records divisions of the National Archives."

354
– – – List of cartographic records of the Bureau of Indian Affairs (Record group 75) Compiled by Laura E. Kelsay. Washington, 1954. 127 p. (*Its* Publication 55-1. Special lists, no. 13)   CD3035.B8U5

"The cartographic records amount to 198 cubic feet and are in the form of manuscript drawings, annotated maps, tracings, blue-prints, ozalids and other photographic copies and printed maps."

355
– – – List of cartographic records of the General Land Office (Record group 49) Compiled by Laura E. Kelsay. Washington, 1964. 202 p. (*Its* Publication no. 64-9. Special list no. 19)   CD3035.G4A5

The maps are described in four groups, i.e., manuscript and annotated maps, boundary survey maps and diagrams, field notes and related records, and published maps.

356
– – – Preliminary inventory of the cartographic records of the American Commission to Negotiate Peace (Record group 256) Compiled by James Berton Rhoads. Washington, 1954. 11 p. (*Its* Publication no. 54-18. Preliminary inventories, no. 68)   CD3026.A32 no. 68

Included are 1,150 items, those records of the Commission "that are separately maintained in the National Archives."

357
– – – Preliminary inventory of the cartographic records of the American Expeditionary Forces, 1917-21 (Record group 120) Compiled by Franklin W. Burch. Washington, 1966. 70 p. (*Its* Publication no. 66-4. Preliminary inventories, no. 165)   CD3026.A32 no. 165

"Most of the maps in this record group were made, collected, or used at General Headquarters, but there was no single map file." There are some 24,000 items in the record group.

358

– – – Preliminary inventory of the cartographic records of the Bureau of the Census (Record group 29) Compiled by James Berton Rhoads and Charlotte M. Ashby. Washington, 1958. 108 p. (*Its* Publication no. 58-6. Preliminary inventories, no. 103)   CD3026.A32 no. 103

"The cartographic records described in this inventory number approximately 30,000 items."

359

– – – Preliminary inventory of the cartographic records of the Federal Housing Administration (Record group 31) Compiled by Charlotte Munchmeyer [Ashby]. Washington, 1952. 57 p. (*Its* Publication no. 53-1. Preliminary inventories, no. 45)   CD3026.A32 no. 45

"The records described . . . comprise the separately maintained cartographic and related records of the Federal Housing Administration for the period 1934 to 1942, now in the National Archives." They number 1,053 items.

360

– – – Preliminary inventory of the cartographic records of the Forest Service (Record group 95) Compiled by Charlotte M. Ashby. Washington, 1967. 71 p. (*Its* Publication no. 67-5. Preliminary inventories, no. 167)
    CD3026.A32 no. 167

"The records described . . . are the map files of the Forest Service that were in the National Archives on September 22, 1966. . . . There are 14,737 discrete items."

361

– – – Preliminary inventory of the cartographic records of the Office of the Chief of Naval Operations (Record group 38) Compiled by Charlotte M. Ashby. Washington, 1955. 17 p. (*Its* Publication no. 56-3. Preliminary inventories, no. 85)   CD3026.A32 no. 85

This preliminary inventory includes 297 items.

362

– – – Preliminary inventory of the cartographic records of the Office of the Secretary of the Interior (Record group 48) Compiled by Laura E. Kelsay. Washington, 1955. 11 p. (*Its* Publication no. 55-13. Preliminary inventories, no. 81)   CD3026.A32 no. 81

The 582 cartographic items include some records transferred to Interior from other units of the government during the early years of that department.

363
– – – Preliminary inventory of the cartographic records of the Panama Canal (Record group 185) Compiled by James Berton Rhoads. Washington, 1956. 72 p. (*Its* Publication no. 56-9. Preliminary inventories, no. 91)

CD3026.A32 no. 91

The approximately 9,240 items constitute only a part of the cartographic records in this record group.

364
– – – Preliminary inventory of the records of the United States Antarctic Service (Record group 126) Compiled by Charles E. Dewing and Laura E. Kelsay. Washington, 1955. 59 p. (*Its* Publication no. 56-8. Preliminary inventories, no. 90)

CD3026.A32 no. 90

"List of cartographic and related records": p. 53-59.

"The records described . . . are all those of the U.S. Antarctic Service that were in the custody of the National Archives on July 1, 1965."

365
– – – Preliminary inventory of the cartographic records of the United States Marine Corps (Record group 127) Compiled by Charlotte M. Ashby. Washington, 1954. 17 p. (*Its* Publication no. 55-4. Preliminary inventories, no. 73)

CD3026.A32 no. 73

Includes 1,608 items.

366
– – – United States scientific geographical exploration of the Pacific Basin, 1783-1899. [Washington, 1961] 26 p. (*Its* Publication no. 62-2)

Z4501.U55

This exhibit was prepared by Herman R. Friis for the Tenth Pacific Science Conference, Honolulu, Hawaii, Aug. 21-Sept. 6, 1969.

367
Uricoechea, Ezequiel. Mapoteca colombiana. Coleccion de los titulos de todos los mapas, planos, vistas etc. relativos á la América Española, Brasil é islas adjacentes. Londres, Trübner & cie, 1860. 215 p.   Z6027.A5U45

Following an introductory essay on the history of American cartography, the maps are arranged by country.

368
Uruguay. *Servicio de Hidrografía.* Catálogo del archivo cartografico histórico. [Montevideo] 1956. 393 p. illus., maps.   Z6028.U7

The annotated titles are arranged by classed groups, such as atlases, planispheres, continental maps, American continent. Also included are an author index, a bibliography of reference works, and brief biographical sketches of notable cartographers.

369

Uzielli, Gustavo, *and* P. Amat de S. Filippo. Mappamondi, carte nautiche, portolani ed altri monumenti cartografici specialmente italiani dei secoli XIII-XVII. Amsterdam, Meridian Pub. Co., 1967. 325 p.   Z6001.U9 1967

Bibliography: p. [303]-312.

Unabridged reprint of Studi biografici e bibliografici sulla storia della geografia in Italia, v. II., 2d ed. (Roma 1882).

An annotated list of more than 500 mappae mundi, nautical charts, portolan charts, and other Italian cartographic treasures of the 13th to the 17th centuries. In addition to an introductory essay, there are a bibliography, a list of names, and an index.

370

Venice. *Commune di Venezia.* Vincenzo Coronelli; nel terzo centenario dalla nascita. Venice, C. Ferrari, 1950. 75 p. illus.   G69.C76V4

Booklet prepared to commemorate the 300th anniversary of the birth of Vincenzo Coronelli. Includes maps by Roberto Almagià and Rodolfo Gallo and a catalog of the exhibit held in Galleria Napoleonica in Piazza S. Marco.

371

Verner, Coolie. The identification and designation of variants in the study of early printed maps. Imago Mundi, v. 19, 1965: 100-105.   GA1.I6 1965

"Cartobibliographical description is the systematic study of early printed maps as objects for the diffusion of geographical knowledge. . . . In the study of variants, the two basic problems encountered involve this identification of plates and the detection of alterations to plates. Each problem must be handled differently."

372

– – – Maps of the Yorktown campaign 1780-1781; a preliminary checklist of printed and manuscript maps prior to 1800. London, Map Collectors' Circle, 1965. 64 p. (Map Collectors' Circle. Map collectors' series, no. 18)

Z6003.M3 no. 18

Bibliography: p. 61-63.

A cartobibliographic study of the maps of the Yorktown, Va., region related to the American Revolution.

373

− − − Smith's Virginia and its derivatives; a carto-bibliographical study of the diffusion of geographical knowledge. London, Map Collectors' Circle, 1968. 40 p. maps. (Map Collectors' Circle. Map collectors' series, no. 45)

Z6003.M3 no. 45

"The carto-bibliographical description and analysis of an important proto-type map will often clarify the way in which geographical information is diffused in the map and chart trade. The study reported here shows something of the sequence through which the first delineation of the Chesapeake Bay became a part of geographical knowledge."

374

Vilnay, Zev. The Holy Land in old prints and maps. Rendered from the Hebrew by Esther Vilnay in collaboration with Max Nurock. 2d ed. enl. Jerusalem, R. Mass [1965] 296 p. illus., maps.   DS108.5.V763 1965

There are 521 illustrations, including reproductions of a number of early maps of the Holy Land. The introductory text summarizes the history and development of early maps and illustrations. Includes bibliographies.

375

Vredenberg-Alink, J. J. Spiegel der wereld. Utrecht, A. Oosthoek, 1969. 112 p. illus., maps.   GA921.V7

Bibliography: p. 127-129.

A small, well-illustrated general history of cartography, in Dutch, with major emphasis on maps and mapping of the Netherlands.

376

Vrij, Y. Marijke de. The world on paper. A descriptive catalogue of carto-graphical material published in Amsterdam during the seventeenth century, by Marijke de Vrij. Amsterdam, Theatrum Orbis Terrarum, 1967. 104 p. illus.   GA925.A43V7 1967

Bibliography: p. 122-123.

Also published in Amsterdam by Amsterdams Historisch Museum, 1967.

GA925.A43V7 1967b

An illustrated catalog with explanatory text which was "compiled for the exhibition at the occasion of the 3d International Conference on Cartography in Amsterdam, April 1967." The text, in English and Dutch, includes a summary history of cartography.

377

Wagner, Henry Raup. The cartography of the northwest coast of America to the year 1800. Amsterdam, N. Israel, 1968. 2 v. in 1. maps.

GA401.W3 1968

"List of Maps": p. 273-364.
Bibliography: p. 527-543.

Reprint of the University of California Press (Berkeley) 1937 edition.

GA401.W3

Although emphasis is on the northwest coast of America, this is a useful reference work for the student of the cartographical history of America. It contains an extensive index, bibliography, and list of place names, as well as a list of maps. An exhaustive and scholarly publication, which includes a note on practically every important map of the world between 1507 and 1794.

378
Waters, David W. The art of navigation in England in Elizabethan and early Stuart times. New Haven, Yale University Press, 1958. 696 p. illus., maps.

VK549.W3

"I have written [this book] not as an instruction for mariners or sailors but as an introduction for such as are desirous to learn what belonged to a seaman in the days when Englishmen first ventured upon the ocean seas." There are 33 documentary appendixes and an extensive bibliography.

379
Wauwermans, Henri Emmanuel. Histoire de l'école cartographique belge et anversoise du XVIe siècle. Bruxelles, Institut National de Géographie, 1895. 2 v. illus., maps.

GA901.W35

An auxiliary work dealing with the history of cartography from early times to the 17th century, with emphasis on the contributions of Belgian and Antwerp mapmakers. A narrative without a general index.

380
Weisz, Leo. Die Schweiz auf alten Karten. Mit Geleitw. und einem kartographisch-technischen Anhang von Ed. Imhof. 2. Aufl. Zürich, Buchverlag der Neuen Zürcher Zeitung, 1969. 247 p. illus., maps.

GA1021.W5 1969

Bibliography: p. 242-245.

A good general history of the cartography of Switzerland, well illustrated with portraits of mapmakers, maps, triangulations, surveying instruments, etc. Unfortunately, it lacks a general index.

381
Wheat, Carl I. Mapping the American West, 1540-1857; a preliminary study. Worcester, Mass., American Antiquarian Society, 1954. [19]-194 p. map.

GA408 1540.W4W4

"Reprinted from the Proceedings of the American Antiquarian Society for April 1954."   E172.A35 v. 64

Bibliographical footnotes.

This is a prelude to his *Mapping the Transmississippi West.*

382
– – – Mapping the transmississippi West, 1540-1880. San Francisco, Institute of Historical Cartography, 1957-60. 5 v. maps.   GA405.W5

Contents:–v. 1. The Spanish entrada to the Louisiana Purchase, 1540-1804. 264 p.–v. 2. From Lewis and Clark to Frémont, 1804-1845. 281 p.–v. 3. From the Mexican War to the boundary surveys, 1846-1854. 349 p.–v. 4. From the Pacific Railroad surveys to the onset of the Civil War, 1855-1860. 260 p.–v. 5 (2 parts). From the Civil War to the Geological Survey [1861-ca. 1880] . 487 p.

Volume 1 gives a general background of the work and "a narrative discussion of the growth and spread of knowledge concerning the Transmississippi region over the period from 1540 to 1804, as disclosed on the maps, and a detailed Bibliocartography presenting data respecting all maps considered." A comprehensive cartobibliography with many fine reproductions.

383
– – – The maps of the California gold region, 1848-1857, a bibliocartography of an important decade. San Francisco, The Grabhorn Press, 1942. 152 p. maps.   Z6027.C15W5

The list is based on an examination of the maps in "all the larger collections of cartography and of Western Americana known to the [compiler]." There are descriptions of 323 maps in a chronological sequence, and an alphabetical index. A limited edition of 300 copies.

384
Wheat, James Clements, *and* Christian F. Brun. Maps and charts published in America before 1800, a bibliography. New Haven, Yale University Press, 1969. 215 p. maps.   Z6027.A5W68

Bibliography: p. 187-207.

"This is the first [list] which attempts to describe the entire known cartographical contribution of the American press prior to 1800. Included are not only the maps and charts published separately but also those used as illustrations in books and pamphlets and from all other sources such as atlases, gazetteers, almanacs, and magazines."

385
Whitehill, Walter Muir. Boston, a topographical history. Cambridge, Belknap Press of Harvard University Press, 2d ed., enl., 1968. 299 p. illus., maps.
                                                    F73.3.W57 1968

Includes reproductions of a number of early maps of Boston, bibliographical notes, and references to the development of the cartography of Boston.

386

Wieder, Frederik Caspar, *ed.* Monumenta cartographica; reproductions of unique and rare maps, plans and views in the actual size of the originals; accompanied by cartographical monographs. The Hague, M. Nijhoff, 1925-33. 5 v. illus., maps. G1025.W5 1925 G&M

In portfolios.

This work, sumptuously prepared, highlights Dutch contributions to exploration and discovery, with emphasis on Petrus Plancius, Joan Vingboons, Willem Janszoon Blaeu, and Abel Janszoon Tasman.

387

Williamson, James A. The Cabot voyages and Bristol discovery under Henry VII. With the cartography of the voyages by R. A. Skelton. Cambridge [Eng.], published for the Hakluyt Society at the University Press, 1962. 332 p. maps. (Hakluyt Society. Works, 2d ser., no. 120)

G161.H2 2d ser., no. 120
E127.W7

Bibliography: p. xv-xvi.

Skelton's contribution on maps "may well have its effect on the controversies that have arisen concerning [the voyages] and will certainly add to the book a stamp of authority which it needs."—Preface.

388

Winsor, Justin, *ed.* Narrative and critical history of America. Boston, Houghton, Mifflin [1884]-89. 8 v. illus., maps. E18.W766

Contains references to so many maps relating to all phases of American history as to be virtually a history of American cartography. Each volume has an extensive index, and volume 8 has a consolidated index. The volumes throughout are illustrated with numerous facsimiles and sketches of maps of historical importance.

389

Wolkenhauer, Wilhelm. Aus der Geschichte der Kartographie. *In* Deutsche geographische Blätter, v. 35, no. 1-2, 1912, p. 29-47; v. 27, no. 2, 1904, p. 95-116; v. 33, no. 4, 1910, p. 239-264; v. 36, no. 3-4, 1913, p. 136-158; v. 38, no. 1, 1916/17, p. 101-128; v. 38, no. 2, 1917, p. 157-201.   G1.D2

Contents:—[no. 1] Die mittelalterliche Kartographie (388-1474).—[no. 2] Von der Wiedererweckung des Ptolemäus bis zu Mercator (1475-1553).—[no. 3] Das Reformzeitalter der Kartographie (1538-1613).—[no. 4] Das Zeitalter des Ubergangs, 1600 bis 1750.—[no. 5] Die Periode der Triangulation und topographischen Aufnahmen (1750-1840).—[no. 6] Die moderne Kartographie (1840-1917).

An expansion of the author's *Leitfaden zur Geschichte der Kartographie,* published in 1895. A chronological record of events important in the development of cartography, notable maps, publications, instruments, and discoveries.

390
Wood, Richard G. Stephen Harriman Long, 1784-1864: army engineer, explorer, inventor. Glendale, Calif., A. H. Clark Co., 1966. 292 p. illus., maps. (Frontier military series, 6)   UG128.L6W6

Bibliography: p. [271]-282.

"Long contributed much to technological advancement in a wide field of endeavors ranging from topography to the design of steam engines and bridges. . . . In his early career, the expeditions he organized and led into the west were a credit to scientific effort."

391
Woodward, David. A bibliography of papers on history of cartography in American periodicals of bibliographical interest found in the libraries of the University of Wisconsin. Madison, University of Wisconsin, Geography Dept., Jan. 1968. 13 l.   G&M Div.

An alphabetical list of 36 serials and an author list with 84 entries.

392
Wright, John K. The geographical lore of the time of the Crusades; a study in the history of medieval science and tradition in Western Europe. With a new introduction by Clarence J. Glacken. New York, Dover Publications [1965] 563 p. illus., maps.   G89.W7 1965

"Unabridged and corrected republication of the work first published by the American Geographical Society of New York in 1925."   G89.W7

Bibliography: [503]-543.

An auxiliary reference work for the student of medieval cartography. Chapter 11 (p. 247-257) contains a critical summary of the maps of the Middle Ages.

393
Wroth, Lawrence Counselman. The early cartography of the Pacific. (*In* Bibliographical Society of America. Papers. New York, 1944. v. 38, no. 2, 1944: 87-268. 22 maps)   Z1008.B51P, v. 38, no. 2

An excellent study of those maps from Ptolemy to 1798 important in the development of the cartography of the Pacific area, with facsimiles of 22 of the 104 maps described.

394
— — — The voyages of Giovanni da Verrazzano, 1524-1528. New Haven, Yale University Press, 1970. 319 p. illus., maps.   E133.V5W7

Bibliography: p. 279-287; map list, p. [288]-305.

Authoritative study of Verrazano and of his discoveries and explorations in North America.

395
Yonge, Ena L. A catalogue of early globes, made prior to 1850 and conserved in the United States; a preliminary listing. New York, American Geographical Society, 1968. 118 p. illus. (Library Series, no. 6)   GA193.U546
Bibliography: p. 118.

Approximately 400 globes, armillary spheres, and orreries are listed. There is an alphabetical list, with brief biographical data, of the 93 globemakers whose works are noted.   .

396
Yūsuf Kamāl, *Prince.* Hallucinations scientifiques (les portulans). Leiden, E. J. Brill, 1937. 95 p. illus., maps.   VK874.A3Y8

"Attempts to disillusion our minds of two so-called 'hallucinations' regarding origin [of portolan charts]: one, that the early charts bear witness to Arabic influence and, two, that anything definite is, in fact, known about their origin." Includes a number of admirable collotype reproductions.

397
– – – Monumenta cartographica Africae et Aegypti. [Le Caire] 1926-51. 5 v. in 16. illus., maps.   G2445.Y8 G&M

Although this work is not a general history of cartography, it is comprehensive for the pre-Ptolemaic and the classical periods. It includes facsimiles of hundreds of maps as well as source materials related to them in Greek, Latin, Arabic, Egyptian, and other languages, all of which are also translated into French. It was published in a limited edition of 70 sets which Prince Yūsuf Kamāl presented to selected institutions throughout the world. In the United States, sets are to be found at the American Geographical Society of New York, the New York Public Library, the Library of Congress, the University of Chicago Library, and the University of California at Los Angeles. The individual maps are indexed under item 10090 in the *List of Geographical Atlases in the Library of Congress,* v. 6, 1963.

398
Zerlik, Alfred. P. Xaver Ernbert Fridelli, Chinamissionar und Kartograph aus Linz. Linz, Oberösterreichischer Landesverlag, 1962. 68 p. illus., maps.
GA1123.6.F7Z4

"Dieses Buch erschien auch als Heft 3/4 der Oberösterreichischen Heimatblätter Jahrgang 16/1962."

About Fridelli, an 18th-century Austrian missionary and cartographer, and his work in China. Fridelli went to China in 1706, where he assisted in surveying and mapping portions of the country. The book includes a list of early 18th-century maps of China, with the names of the cartographers (among them Fridelli) who compiled them. There are 39 illustrations, many of them map reproductions, in the volume.

Index

This index contains references to subjects, geographical areas, and secondary authors and contributors.

Brazil: cartography, 132; map collections, 53, 54, 56, 120, 132, 163; maps, 2, 55, 56, 262, 367
British Admiralty Hydrographic Service, 89
Brouwer, G. J., 232
Brun, Christian F., 220, 384
Burch, Franklin W., 357
Byelorussia, 251

Cabot, John, 157, 387
California: gold region, 383; land grants, 35; maps, 69, 137, 141
California, University of, map collections; see Bancroft Library
Canada: cartography, 121, 331; cities, 212; discovery and exploration, 37; hydrography, 100; maps, 68, 93, 320; surveying, 331; see also North America
Cape Colony, southern Africa, cartography, 185
Cartier, Jacques, 158
Cartobibliography, 27, 47, 85, 115, 205, 250, 305, 366, 371
Cartographers; see Mapmakers
Cartography, general histories, 20, 23-25, 27, 57, 61, 81, 97, 112, 157, 160, 171, 175, 176, 198, 200, 203, 204, 273, 288, 306, 332, 338, 375, 376, 389, 391; ancient, 64, 80, 138, 153, 192, 193, 201, 242, 243, 259, 285, 397; bibliographies of, 12, 41, 187, 347, 391; medieval, 34, 80, 165, 166, 178, 201, 242, 243, 285, 290, 379, 392; nautical, 28, 107, 122, 131; post-1600, 80, 152, 303; Renaissance, 22, 40, 77, 80, 242, 257, 285, 303, 379; see also names of countries, areas, and cities
Central America, 164, 228; see also Latin America
Ceylon, 300
Champlain, Lake, 159
Charlestown, Mass., 212
Chile, 216, 263
China: cartography, 172, 236, 398; maps, 21, 43; portolan charts, 172
Cincinnati, Ohio, 212
Civil War, American, maps, 343, 344, 351
Clements, William L., Library, Michigan University, 219, 220
Clinton, Sir Henry, 219
Collijn, Isak, 210
Colombia, 76
Commerce and trade, 225, 226
Connecticut, 328, 329
Cook, Capt. James, 301
Coronelli, Vicenzo, 370
Coronelli-Weltbund der Globus Freunde, 126
Correia, Maximino, 79

Cortambert, M. E., 171
Costa Rica, 164, 253
Crone, Gerald R., 57, 166
Cuba, 340
Czechoslovakia, 193

Day, Archibald, 42
Day, James M., 325
De Brahm, William, 93
Delkeskamp, Friedrich Wilhelm, 208
Denmark: cartography, 51, 123; maps, 51, 241
Des Barres, J. F. W., 100
Destombes, Marcel, 165, 166, 254
Detroit, Mich., 212
Deutsche Gesellschaft für Kartographie, 41
Dewing, Charles E., 360
Discovery and exploration, general histories, 7, 8, 34, 152, 155, 226, 257, 299, 304, 310; see also names of continents, countries, and other geographical areas
District of Columbia, 212, 276, 346
Doneghy, Virginia, 37
Drake, Sir Francis, 188
Düsseldorf, Germany, 156
Dunlap, Ann B., 325

Ebeling, C. D., 148
Ebenezer, Ga., 212
Eddy, Henry Howard, 244
Edgell, John, 283
Edward E. Ayer Collection; see Ayer, Edward E., Collection
Egypt, 397; see also Africa
Ekelöf, Johan Adolf, 242
Eldridge, Winfield H., 11
Eller, Robert C., 11
Emmison, F. G., 99
England: estate maps, 99; maps, 70; see also Great Britain
Engravers; see Mapmakers, engravers
Exhibits, 27, 38, 62, 86, 95, 135, 268, 286, 352, 365, 370, 376
Explorations; see Discovery and exploration

Faber, Konrad, 208
Facsimile maps and atlases, 82, 101, 199, 210, 217, 274, 281, 326, 386
Falkland Islands, 228
Fauser, A., 101
Ferrande (Pierre Garcie), 122
Ferrara, Italy, 49
Florida, 311
Fonçin, Myriem, 254
France: cartography, 115, 116; exploration in New World, 16; globes, 117; portolan charts, 16, 254; road books, 115; sailing guides, 122

94

☆ U. S. GOVERNMENT PRINTING OFFICE : 1973 O - 507-937